Table of Contents

Introduction

Are you aware of the idea of a macro diet? Do you want to have a diet that can provide just enough amount of proteins, fats and carbohydrates? Well, a macro diet can help you optimize the intake of these macro nutrients, which will help you achieve good health. In this cookbook, you will find more than seventy delicious recipes with a 4-week meal plan to easily incorporate a macro diet into your lifestyle.

What is a Macro diet?

The macro diet provides a simple approach to keep track of the nutrients we consume. Instead of focusing on the caloric intakes, this diet takes the number of macro nutrients like carbohydrate, proteins and fats into consideration. It is these macros that play a major role in our metabolism; carbs are an instant source of energy, proteins provide amino acids for building muscles, and fats are the long-term secondary source of energy. By optimizing the intake of these nutrients, a person can achieve good health. According to the macro diet, there has to be a balanced intake of these macronutrients. This intake must be according to the needs of the human body. According to this diet, a meal has to have 10-35 per cent proteins, 20-35 per cent fats and 45-65 per cent carbs.

Benefits of Macro Diet

Macro diet is great because it does not provide one-size-fits-all formula. Rather it offers a flexible diet plan which anyone can use according to his needs. If a person is striving for weight loss, he or she can minimize the intake of fat and carbs.

Macro-nutrients are responsible for controlling all of our metabolism. The macro diet focuses on the importance of each of these nutrients and provides them in the perfect quantity, which boosts metabolism, helps rejuvenate cells and provide energy without causing weight gain.

Breakfast and Brunch

Breakfast Caprese With Eggs

Prep Time: 10 minutes.

Cook Time: 6 minutes.

Serves: 2

Ingredients:

- 2 large eggs
- 3 thin slices mozzarella
- 1 small tomato, sliced
- 1 teaspoon olive oil
- Fresh basil leaves, for serving
- Salt and black pepper, to taste

Preparation:

1. Boil egg in water in a pot filled with water for 6 minutes.
2. Transfer the eggs to an ice bath, peel once cooled.
3. Arrange the tomato and mozzarella slices in a plate to make a round with a circle at the center.
4. Add eggs to the center and drizzle oil, black pepper, basil and salt on top.
5. Serve.

Serving Suggestion: Serve the caprese with crispy bacon on the side.

Variation Tip: Add a dollop of mayonnaise on top before serving.

Nutritional Information Per Serving:

Calories 184 | Fat 19g |Sodium 704mg | Carbs 6g | Fiber 3.6g | Sugar 6g | Protein 18g

Blueberry Breakfast Cake

Prep Time: 15 minutes.

Cook Time: 60 minutes.

Serves: 6

Ingredients:

- 1 cup unsweetened applesauce
- ¼ cup pure maple syrup
- ½ cup coconut sugar
- ½ cup almond butter
- 1 cup unsweetened almond milk
- 1½ teaspoon pure vanilla extract
- 1¾ cups 2 tablespoons spelt flour
- ½ cup old-fashioned rolled oats
- 2 teaspoons ground cinnamon
- 1½ teaspoon baking powder
- 1 teaspoon ground ginger
- ½ teaspoon ground nutmeg
- ½ teaspoon ground allspice
- ¼ teaspoon baking soda
- ¼ teaspoon fine sea salt
- 1½ cups frozen blueberries
- ½ cup shelled pistachios, chopped

Preparation:

1. At 350 degrees F, preheat your oven.
2. Line a 9x5 inches loaf pan with parchment paper.
3. Mix vanilla extract, almond milk, almond butter, coconut sugar, maple syrup and applesauce.
4. Mix baking soda, salt, allspice, nutmeg, ginger, baking powder, cinnamon, rolled oats, and 1 ¾ spelt flour in a bowl.
5. Stir in almond milk mixture and mix well.
6. Toss blueberries with 2 tablespoons spelt flour in a bowl.
7. Add the berries and chopped pistachios to the batter then mix evenly.
8. Spread this batter in the loaf pan and bake for 60 minutes.
9. Allow the cake to cool and slice.
10. Serve.

Serving Suggestion: Serve the cake with maple syrup on top.

Variation Tip: Add berry sauce on top of the cake.

Nutritional Information Per Serving:

Calories 134 | Fat 4.7g |Sodium 1mg | Carbs 14.1g | Fiber 7g | Sugar 3.3g | Protein 6g

Oatmeal with Crispy Bacon

Prep Time: 15 minutes.

Cook Time: 3 hrs. 15 minutes.

Serves: 2

Ingredients:

- 1 ¼ cups gluten free rolled oats
- 1 cup peeled squash, diced
- 1 tablespoon butter
- 2 tablespoons flaxseed
- 1 teaspoon garlic, minced
- 1 teaspoon sea salt
- Pinch of black pepper
- ½ cup cherry tomatoes, sliced
- ¼ cup parmesan cheese, shredded
- 1 teaspoon red pepper flakes
- 3/4 cup broth
- 2 cup almond milk
- ½ cup water

Crispy Bacon

- 1 ½ ounces uncured bacon strips
- 1/4 cup red onion, sliced

Preparation:

1. Mix parmesan, broth, milk, seasoning, garlic. Flaxseed, butter, tomato, squash and oats in a slow cooker.
2. Cover and cook on High setting for 3 hours.
3. Meanwhile, spread bacon and onion in a baking sheet lined with foil.
4. Bake the bacon for 15 minutes in the oven. at 350 degrees F.
5. Divide the oatmeal's in the bowls and garnish with onions and bacon.
6. Serve.

Serving Suggestion: Serve the oatmeal with toasted bread.

Variation Tip: Replace squash with zucchini.

Nutritional Information Per Serving:

Calories 217 | Fat 3g |Sodium 114mg | Carbs 23.1g | Fiber 1g | Sugar 10g | Protein 10g

Skillet Eggs and Chorizo

Prep Time: 10 minutes.

Cook Time: 11 minutes.

Serves: 4

Ingredients:

- 1 tablespoon olive oil
- ½ lb. Mexican chorizo, casings removed
- 2 jalapeños, chopped
- 2 (14-ounce) cans diced tomatoes
- 4 garlic cloves, crushed
- 2 teaspoons granulated sugar
- 1 teaspoon chipotle chili flakes
- Salt and black pepper, to taste
- 4 large eggs
- 2 ounces feta cheese, crumbled
- 2 large handfuls parsley, chopped
- Sour cream, for serving

Preparation:

1. Sauté chorizo with olive oil and in a skillet for 5 minutes.
2. Stir in jalapeno and cook for 1 minute.
3. Add garlic and tomatoes then cook on high heat until tomatoes bubbles.
4. Add chili flakes, sugar, black pepper and salt then cook for 5 minutes.
5. Make 4 small well in this tomato mixture and crack on egg in each.
6. Drizzle parsley, feta and dollop of sour cream on top.
7. Serve.

Serving Suggestion: Serve the eggs with crispy bread toasts.

Variation Tip: Add chopped zucchini to the mixture before baking.

Nutritional Information Per Serving:

Calories 212 | Fat 12g |Sodium 321mg | Carbs 14.6g | Fiber 4g | Sugar 8g | Protein 17g

Baked Eggs and Zoodles with Avocado

Prep Time: 15 minutes.

Cook Time:11 minutes.

Serves: 4

Ingredients:

- Nonstick spray
- 3 zucchinis, spiralized into noodles
- 2 tablespoons olive oil
- Salt and black pepper, to taste
- 4 large eggs
- Red-pepper flakes, for garnishing
- Fresh basil, for garnishing
- 2 avocados, halved and sliced

Preparation:

1. At 350 degrees F, preheat your oven.
2. Grease a baking sheet with cooking spray.
3. Toss zucchini noodles with olive oil, black pepper and salt in a bowl.
4. Divide this mixture into four portions onto the baking sheet
5. Shape each zucchini portion into a nest and crack one egg in each nest.
6. Bake these egg nests for 11 minutes.
7. Garnish with black pepper, salt, and red pepper flakes.
8. Serve warm with avocado slices.

Serving Suggestion: Serve the eggs with crispy bacon on the side.

Variation Tip: Add spiralized carrots to the zucchini noodles.

Nutritional Information Per Serving:

Calories 112 | Fat 5g |Sodium 132mg | Carbs 4g | Fiber 3.9g | Sugar 3g | Protein 18.9g

Spanish Tortilla with Zucchini

Prep Time: 15 minutes.

Cook Time: 47 minutes.

Serves: 3

Ingredients:

- 1 medium russet potato, sliced
- 2 tablespoons olive oil
- 1 onion, sliced
- ½ zucchini, sliced
- Salt and black pepper, to taste
- 3 large eggs
- 2 tablespoons Manchego cheese, grated

Preparation:

1. At 400 degrees F, preheat your oven.
2. Add water and potatoes to a saucepan and cook them for 25 minutes.
3. Drain the boiled potato and keep it aside.
4. Sauté zucchini and onion with oil, black pepper and salt in a skillet for 4 minutes.
5. Stir in veggies and potatoes slice then cook for 7 minutes.
6. Beat eggs and pour over the veggies then drizzle the cheese on top.
7. Bake the eggs for 15 minutes in the oven.
8. Slice and serve warm.

Serving Suggestion: Serve the eggs with crispy bacon.

Variation Tip: Add chopped mushrooms to the eggs.

Nutritional Information Per Serving:

Calories 331 | Fat 2.5g |Sodium 595mg | Carbs 9g | Fiber 12g | Sugar 12g | Protein 19g

Lemon Poppyseed Muffins with Blueberry Glaze

Prep Time: 15 minutes.

Cook Time: 15 minutes.

Serves: 6

Ingredients:

- 1 ½ cups whole wheat pastry flour
- 1 ½ teaspoon baking powder
- ½ teaspoon baking soda
- 1/4 teaspoon salt
- 2 tablespoons poppy seeds
- Wet ingredients
- Zest from 2 large lemons
- ½ cup honey
- 2 large eggs
- ½ cup plain yogurt
- 2 tablespoons lemon juice
- ½ teaspoon almond extract
- ¼ cup butter, melted

Glaze:

- ⅓ cup powdered sugar
- 1 tablespoon blueberry preserves
- 1 teaspoon lemon zest
- 1 teaspoon fresh lemon juice
- ½ tablespoon melted butter

Preparation:

1. At 400 degrees F, preheat your oven.
2. Grease 9 cups of a 12-cup muffin pan with cooking spray.
3. Mix poppyseeds, salt, baking soda, baking powder, and flour in a bowl.
4. Beat eggs with yogurt, almond extract, lemon juice, honey and lemon zest in a bowl.
5. Stir in flour-poppyseeds mixture along with butter.
6. Mix well then divide this batter in the greased muffin cups.
7. Bake these poppyseed muffins for 15 minutes in the oven.
8. Meanwhile, for glaze mix with butter, with lemon juice, lemon zest, sugar and blueberry jam in a saucepan.

9. Divide this glaze on top of the muffins.

10. Serve.

Serving Suggestion: Serve the muffins with green smoothie.

Variation Tip: Add some blueberries to the muffin batter.

Nutritional Information Per Serving:

Calories 322 | Fat 12g |Sodium 202mg | Carbs 14.6g | Fiber 4g | Sugar 8g | Protein 7.3g

Egg Avocado Bowl

Prep Time: 10 minutes.

Cook Time: 0 minutes.

Serves: 2

Ingredients:

- 1 cup Greek yogurt
- 1 cup cooked brown rice
- 2 eggs, boiled
- 1 avocado, sliced
- juice from 1 lemon
- 2 tablespoons bagel spice
- 1 cup arugula
- 1 pinch flaky sea salt
- Olive oil, to garnish
- Chopped chives, for serving

Preparation:

1. Divide the yogurt in tow serving bowls.
2. Add eggs, avocado, brown rice, lemon juice, spices, greens and olive oil on top.
3. Serve.

Serving Suggestion: Serve these bowls with fresh muffins on the side.

Variation Tip: Add crispy bacon on top.

Nutritional Information Per Serving:

Calories 197 | Fat 15g |Sodium 548mg | Carbs 9g | Fiber 4g | Sugar 1g | Protein 17.9g

Scrambled Tofu Burrito

Prep Time: 15 minutes.

Cook Time: 38 minutes.

Serves: 4

Ingredients:

Tofu

- 1 (12-ounce) package extra-firm tofu
- 1 teaspoon cooking oil
- 3 garlic cloves, minced
- 1 tablespoon hummus
- ½ teaspoon chili powder
- ½ teaspoon cumin
- 1 teaspoon nutritional yeast
- 1/4 teaspoon sea salt
- 1 pinch cayenne pepper
- 1/4 cup parsley, minced

Vegetables

- 5 whole baby potatoes, chopped
- 1 medium red bell pepper, sliced
- 1 teaspoon olive oil
- 1 pinch sea salt
- ½ teaspoon ground cumin
- ½ teaspoon chili powder
- 2 cups kale, chopped

Rest

- 4 large flour tortillas
- 1 medium ripe avocado, chopped
- Cilantro
- Chunky red or green salsa

Preparation:

1. At 400 degrees F, preheat your oven.

2. Layer a baking sheet with parchment paper.

3. Press and squeeze the tofu to remove the excess water.

4. Spread potatoes with red pepper in the baking sheet and drizzle spices and oil on top.

5. Bake these potatoes for 18 minutes then add kale on top.

6. Continue cooking for another 5 minutes and toss well.

7. Sauté garlic with and tofu in a suitable skillet for 10 minutes.

8. Mix hummus with cayenne, salt, yeast, cumin, and chili powder in a small bowl.

9. Add this hummus mixture to the tofu and cook for 5 minutes while scrambling it.

10. Spread a large tortilla on the working surface and top it with ¼ of roasted vegetables, avocado, tofu, cilantro and salsa.

11. Roll the tortilla into a burrito and serve.

12. Repeat the same steps with remaining tortillas and filling.

13. Serve.

Serving Suggestion: Serve the burrito with a drizzle of cheese on top.

Variation Tip: Add some shredded cabbage to the filling.

Nutritional Information Per Serving:

Calories 218 | Fat 22g |Sodium 350mg | Carbs 12.2g | Fiber 0.7g | Sugar 1g | Protein 14.3g

Vegetable Frittatas

Prep Time: 15 minutes.

Cook Time: 17 minutes.

Serves: 8

Ingredients:

- 1 red bell pepper, diced
- 1 yellow bell pepper, diced
- 1 zucchini, diced
- 1 small onion, diced
- 1 cup Parmesan cheese, shredded
- 8 eggs, beaten
- 2 tablespoons chives
- Salt and black pepper to taste
- olive oil for drizzling

Preparation:

1. At 350 degrees F, preheat your oven.
2. Sauté zucchini with onion and bell pepper in a skillet for 5 minutes.
3. Stir in black pepper and salt then divide this mixture in a muffin pan.
4. Beat eggs with black pepper, salt, parmesan and chives in a bowl.
5. Divide this blend in the muffin cups and bake for 12 minutes.
6. Serve.

Serving Suggestion: Serve the frittatas with toasted bread slices.

Variation Tip: Add shredded carrot to the frittatas.

Nutritional Information Per Serving:

Calories 157 | Fat 2g |Sodium 48mg | Carbs 6g | Fiber 2g | Sugar 0g | Protein 17g

Poultry

Persian Spiced Roasted Chicken

Prep Time: 10 minutes.

Cook Time: 35 minutes.

Serves: 4

Ingredients:

- 4 chicken thighs
- ½ teaspoon sea salt
- 1 teaspoon turmeric
- ½ teaspoon allspice
- ½ teaspoon cayenne
- 1 pinch of paprika
- 1 pinch of black pepper
- 1 teaspoon garlic, minced
- 3 tablespoons olive oil
- 1 tablespoon lemon juice
- 1-lb. gold new potatoes, quartered
- 1 cup cherry tomatoes, sliced
- Lemon slices for garnish
- Crushed Red pepper flakes to garnish

Preparation:

1. At 375 degrees F, preheat your oven.
2. Rub the chicken thighs with sea salt flakes.
3. Mix 1 tablespoon lemon juice, 4 tablespoons oil, 1 teaspoon garlic, pepper, paprika, ½ teaspoon cayenne, ½ teaspoon allspice, ½ teaspoon salt and 1 teaspoon turmeric in a small bowl.
4. Rub this mixture over the chicken thighs and keep the rest for potatoes.
5. Add potatoes and tomatoes to a skillet and cook for 5 minutes.
6. Place chicken, potatoes and tomatoes in a suitable skillet and cook for 5 minutes on a simmer.
7. Flip the chicken and potatoes.
8. Add the spice mixture, red pepper flakes and lemon slices on top.
9. Bake this mixture for 25 minutes in the oven.
10. Serve warm.

Serving Suggestion: Serve the chicken with roasted asparagus

Variation Tip: Coat the chicken with breadcrumbs before cooking for crisp.

Nutritional Information Per Serving:

Calories 304 | Fat 3g |Sodium 216mg | Carbs 17g | Fiber 3g | Sugar 4g | Protein 21g

Green Bowl with Chicken

Prep Time: 15 minutes.

Cook Time: 10 minutes.

Serves: 2

Ingredients:

- 1 teaspoon olive oil
- 1 small shallot, minced
- ½ teaspoon sea salt
- 1 cup broccoli slaw
- 1 cup asparagus, chopped
- 2 cups baby spinach
- Zest of 1 orange
- 1 teaspoon Za'atar
- 3 ounces cooked chicken, shredded
- ¼ avocado, pitted, peeled and sliced
- ¼ cup green goddess dressing
- Zest of 1 lemon, grated
- ¼ cup fresh herbs, minced

Preparation:

1. Sauté shallots with olive oil, and sea salt in a skillet until soft.
2. Stir in asparagus and broccoli then cook until tender.
3. Add zaatar, orange zest and spinach then cook for 3 minutes.
4. Stir chicken and cook for 2 minutes.
5. Garnish with lemon zest, herbs, and avocado.
6. Serve warm.

Serving Suggestion: Serve the bowls with bean sprouts on top.

Variation Tip: Added chopped nuts to the bowl.

Nutritional Information Per Serving:

Calories 180 | Fat 9g |Sodium 318mg | Carbs 19g | Fiber 5g | Sugar 3g | Protein 17g

Turkey and White Bean Chili

Prep Time: 15 minutes.

Cook Time: 5 hrs. 10 minutes.

Serves: 6

Ingredients:

- 1 tablespoon olive oil
- 2 small yellow onions, chopped
- 4 garlic cloves, minced
- 2 lbs. ground turkey
- 2 red peppers, seeded and chopped
- 2 chipotle peppers in adobo, chopped
- 2 tablespoons chili powder
- 1 tablespoon smoked paprika
- 2 teaspoons ground cumin
- 1 teaspoon ground cinnamon
- 1 ½ teaspoon salt
- 3 cups chicken broth
- 1 can (28 ounce) crushed tomatoes
- 1/4 cup tomato paste
- 1 tablespoon apple butter
- 2 bay leaves
- 1 can (14 ounce) white beans, drained
- Cheddar cheese, green onions, avocado, and cilantro for serving

Preparation:

1. Sauté onion with oil in a large skillet over medium heat for 5 minutes.
2. Stir in turkey and sauté for 5 minutes then remove from the heat.
3. Transfer this turkey mixture to a slow cooker and add rest of the ingredients on top.
4. Cover and cook the turkey for 5 hours on High setting.
5. Garnish with cheddar cheese, green onions, and avocado.
6. Serve warm.

Serving Suggestion: Serve the chili with tortillas chips on top.

Variation Tip: Add corn kernel to the chili.

Nutritional Information Per Serving:

Calories 273 | Fat 8g |Sodium 146mg | Carbs 18g | Fiber 5g | Sugar 1g | Protein 27g

Lemon-Herb Chicken and Avocado Salad

Prep Time: 15 minutes.

Cook Time: 64 minutes.

Serves: 2

Ingredients:

Lemon-Herb Chicken

- 1½ lbs. boneless chicken breasts
- 3 tablespoons olive oil
- Zest and juice of 2 lemons
- 1 tablespoon fresh oregano, chopped
- 1 tablespoon fresh dill, chopped
- 3 tablespoons fresh parsley, chopped
- Salt and black pepper, to taste

Salad

- 1 cup barley
- 2½ cups chicken broth
- Zest and juice of 1 lemon
- 1 tablespoon whole-grain mustard
- 1 teaspoon dried oregano
- ⅓ cup olive oil
- Salt and black pepper, to taste
- 2 heads red-leaf lettuce, chopped
- 1 red onion, halved and thinly sliced
- 1-pint cherry tomatoes, sliced
- 2 avocados, sliced

Preparation:

1. Mix chicken with lemon herb marinade in a ziplock bag.
2. Seal and refrigerate this chicken for 30 minutes for marination.
3. During this time, mix broth with barley in a saucepan and cook for 45 minutes.
4. Drain and transfer the barley to a salad bowl then toss in rest of the salad ingredients.
5. Set a grill over medium heat and grease its grilling grates.
6. Grill the chicken for 12 minutes per side.

7. Serve the chicken with the salad.

Serving Suggestion: Serve the chicken with fresh herbs on top.

Variation Tip: Add crumbled cheese to the salad.

Nutritional Information Per Serving:

Calories 140 | Fat 5g |Sodium 244mg | Carbs 16g | Fiber 1g | Sugar 1g | Protein 17g

Chicken Salad Stuffed Peppers

Prep Time: 10 minutes.

Cook Time: 0 minutes.

Serves: 3

Ingredients:

- ⅔ cup Greek yogurt
- 2 tablespoons Dijon mustard
- 2 tablespoons seasoned rice vinegar
- Salt and black pepper, to taste
- ⅓ cup fresh parsley, chopped
- 1 rotisserie chicken, meat only, cubed
- 4 stalks celery, sliced
- 1 bunch scallions, sliced
- 1-pint cherry tomatoes, quartered
- ½ English cucumber, diced
- 3 bell peppers, halved and seeds removed

Preparation:

1. Mix yogurt with black pepper, salt, vinegar, and mustard in a bowl.
2. Stir in chicken, celery, parsley, cucumber, tomatoes and scallions.
3. Mix well then divide this chicken filling in the bell peppers.
4. Serve.

Serving Suggestion: Serve the stuffed peppers with roasted veggies on the side.

Variation Tip: Add corn kernels to the pepper filling.

Nutritional Information Per Serving:

Calories 282 | Fat 4g |Sodium 232mg | Carbs 7g | Fiber 1g | Sugar 0g | Protein 14g

Harissa Chicken with Chickpeas

Prep Time: 15 minutes.

Cook Time: 45 minutes.

Serves: 2

Ingredients:

- 1 ½ lbs. boneless chicken breasts
- 1/4 cup olive oil
- 2 lemons, juice and zest from
- 2 tablespoons Harissa seasoning
- 1 tablespoon honey
- Salt and black pepper, to taste
- 2 medium sweet potatoes, diced
- 1 sweet onion, sliced
- 1 can (14 ounces) chickpeas, drained

Toppings

- ½ cup crumbled feta
- 1/3 cup green olives, smashed
- Greek yogurt and fresh mint, for serving

Preparation:

1. At 425 degrees F, preheat your oven.
2. Mix chicken with black pepper, salt honey, harissa seasoning, lemon zest, lemon juice, and 2 tablespoons olive oil in a bowl.
3. Spread the coated chicken in a baking sheet.
4. Add sweet potatoes and the rest of the ingredients around the chicken.
5. Bake the chicken mixture for 45 minutes in the oven.
6. Garnish with all the toppings.
7. Serve warm.

Serving Suggestion: Serve the chicken with roasted broccoli florets.

Variation Tip: Add dried herbs to season the chicken.

Nutritional Information Per Serving:

Calories 329 | Fat 5g |Sodium 510mg | Carbs 17g | Fiber 5g | Sugar 4g | Protein 21g

Chicken Tagine with Olives

Prep Time: 15 minutes.

Cook Time: 45 minutes.

Serves: 8

Ingredients:

Chicken

- 8 garlic cloves, chopped
- 1 teaspoon sweet paprika
- 1 teaspoon ground cumin
- ½ teaspoon ground ginger
- ½ teaspoon saffron threads, crushed
- ½ teaspoon turmeric
- Salt and black pepper, to taste
- 8 bone in chicken thighs

Tagine

- 2 tablespoons olive oil
- 3 yellow onions, sliced
- ¼ teaspoon ground cinnamon
- 16 green olives, pitted and smashed

- 1 lemon, zest
- 1 cup chicken stock
- Juice of ½ lemon
- 1 tablespoon parsley, chopped

Preparation:

1. Mix ½ teaspoon black pepper, ½ teaspoon salt, turmeric, cumin, paprika, ginger, saffron and garlic in a bowl.
2. Rub this spice mixture over the chicken, cover and refrigerate for 4 hours.
3. Sear the chicken in a skillet greased with oil until golden brown from both the sides.
4. Transfer the chicken to a plate and add onions to the skillet.
5. Sauté for 15 minutes on low heat until caramelized then add cinnamon.
6. Return the chicken to the skillet then add lemon strips, olives, lemon juice and stock.
7. Cover and cook over low heat for 30 minutes.
8. Garnish with parsley and serve warm.

Serving Suggestion: Serve the chicken with warmed tortillas or rice.

Variation Tip: Drizzle paprika on top for more spice.

Nutritional Information Per Serving:

Calories 201 | Fat 7g |Sodium 269mg | Carbs 15g | Fiber 4g | Sugar 12g | Protein 26g

Chicken Tortilla Soup

Prep Time: 15 minutes.

Cook Time: 7 hrs. 8 minutes.

Serves: 4

Ingredients:

- 1 tablespoon olive oil
- 1-lb. boneless chicken thighs
- 1 white onion, chopped
- 4 garlic cloves, minced
- 2 jalapeños, seeded and diced
- 1 (28 ounce) can fire roasted crushed tomatoes
- 1 (15 ounce) can black beans, rinsed and drained
- 1 cup frozen sweet corn
- 5 cups chicken broth
- 2 teaspoons ancho chili powder
- 2 teaspoons cumin
- ½ teaspoon dried oregano
- ½ teaspoon paprika
- 1/4 teaspoon cayenne pepper
- ½ teaspoon salt
- Black pepper, to taste
- 2 small limes, juiced

Garnish

- Tortilla strips or crushed tortilla chips
- 1 large diced avocado
- Sour cream
- Shredded Monterey jack
- Cilantro
- Diced Green onion

Preparation:

1. Sear the chicken thighs in a skillet with oil for 2 minutes per side.
2. Add black pepper and salt to the chicken for seasoning.

3. Transfer the chicken to a slow cooker.

4. Sauté onions with garlic, jalapeno in the same skillet for 4 minutes.

5. Transfer these sautéed veggies to the slow cooker.

6. Stir in rest of the ingredients, cover and cook for 7 hours on Low heat.

7. Garnish with chips, avocado, sour cream, cheese, cilantro and green onion.

8. Serve warm.

Serving Suggestion: Serve this soup with warmed tortillas

Variation Tip: Add sliced mushrooms to the soup.

Nutritional Information Per Serving:

Calories 348 | Fat 12g |Sodium 710mg | Carbs 14g | Fiber 5g | Sugar 3g | Protein 11g

Thai Peanut Chicken with Coconut Purple Rice

Prep Time: 15 minutes.

Cook Time: 6 hrs. 30 minutes.

Serves: 2

Ingredients:

- 1/3 cup natural peanut butter
- ½ tablespoon honey
- 2 tablespoons soy sauce
- 2 garlic cloves, minced
- 1 tablespoon sriracha
- 1 cup unsweetened almond milk
- 1-lb. boneless chicken breasts
- 1 red bell pepper, sliced
- 1 cup purple rice
- 2 teaspoons coconut oil
- Cilantro and peanuts for garnish

Preparation:

1. Add almond milk, hot sauce, garlic, soy sauce, honey and peanut butter to a slow cooker.
2. Stir in red pepper slices and chicken then cover and cook on Low heat for 6 hours.
3. Shred the cooked chicken and mix with the sauce.
4. Sauté rice with coconut oil in a deep skillet for 5 minutes.
5. Stir in water and cook to a boil then reduce its heat and cook for 25 minutes on a simmer.
6. Divide the rice in the serving bowls and then top with chicken, hot sauce, peanuts and cilantro.
7. Serve warm.

Serving Suggestion: Serve the chicken and rice with mint yogurt sauce.

Variation Tip: Replace almond milk with coconut milk.

Nutritional Information Per Serving:

Calories 375 | Fat 16g |Sodium 255mg | Carbs 31g | Fiber 1.2g | Sugar 5g | Protein 24.1g

Chicken Meatballs with Peanut Sauce

Prep Time: 15 minutes.

Cook Time: 26 minutes.

Serves: 6

Ingredients:

Meatballs

- 1 lb. 93% lean ground chicken
- 1 egg
- ½ cup panko breadcrumbs
- 1/4 cup green onion, chopped
- ¼ cup cilantro, diced
- 1 jalapeño, seeded and diced
- 3 garlic cloves, minced
- 1 tablespoon ginger, grated
- ¼ teaspoon cayenne pepper
- ½ teaspoon salt
- Black pepper, to taste
- 1 tablespoon toasted sesame oil

Peanut sauce

- 1 (15 ounce) can light coconut milk
- ½ cup peanut butter
- 2 tablespoons soy sauce
- 1 tablespoon chili paste

Add-ins:

- 2 carrots, sliced
- 1 red bell pepper, julienned
- 2/3 cup frozen peas

Garnish

- Chopped honey peanuts, roasted
- Diced scallions
- Fresh cilantro

- Hot sauce

Preparation:

1. Mix ground chicken with black pepper, salt, cayenne, ginger, garlic, jalapeno, cilantro, green onion, breadcrumbs, and egg in a bowl.
2. Make 16 meatballs out of this chicken mixture.
3. Sear the meatballs with sesame oil in a deep skillet over medium high heat for 3 minutes per side.
4. Transfer the meatballs to a plate.
5. Reduce its heat and add coconut milk, chili paste, soy sauce and peanut butter to the same skillet.
6. Add carrots and seared meatballs then cover to cook on a simmer for 15 minutes.
7. Remove the lid then add bell pepper and peas then cook for 5 minutes.
8. Serve warm with rice or quinoa.

Serving Suggestion: Serve the chicken meatballs with a kale salad on the side.

Variation Tip: Add shredded cheese to the meatball's mixture.

Nutritional Information Per Serving:

Calories 335 | Fat 25g |Sodium 122mg | Carbs 13g | Fiber 0.4g | Sugar 1g | Protein 33g

Fish and Seafood

Baked Sesame-Ginger Salmon

Prep Time: 15 minutes.

Cook Time: 18 minutes.

Serves: 4

Ingredients:

- 1 teaspoon sesame oil
- 2 tablespoons soy sauce
- 2 tablespoons fresh ginger, grated
- 1 teaspoon garlic powder
- 2 tablespoons honey
- Pinch of red-pepper flakes
- 2 large zucchinis, thinly sliced
- 1 red onion, halved and thinly sliced
- 1 lime, quartered
- 4 (6-ounce) skinless salmon fillets
- 4 teaspoons sesame seeds

Preparation:

1. At 350 degrees F, preheat your oven.
2. Fold four 15x17 inches parchment sheet in half to make a crease then unfold.
3. Mix red pepper flakes, honey, garlic powder, ginger, soy sauce and sesame oil in a small bowl.
4. Place one parchment paper on the working surface and add ¼ zucchini on top.
5. Add ¼ red onion top and drizzle ¼ lime juice on top.
6. Place the salmon fillet on top of these veggies and brush this salmon with the soy sauce mixture.
7. Drizzle 1 teaspoon sesame seeds on top.
8. Fold the parchment paper over the salmon and seal the edges.
9. Repeat the same steps with remaining parchment paper, salmon, sauce, veggies and sesame seeds.
10. Place the salmon packets in the baking sheet and bake for 18 minutes.
11. Serve warm.

Serving Suggestion: Serve the salmon with roasted green beans and mashed potatoes.

Variation Tip: Add sliced carrots to the veggie mixture.

Nutritional Information Per Serving:

Calories 329 | Fat 17g |Sodium 422mg | Carbs 15g | Fiber 0g | Sugar 1g | Protein 41g

Hemp and Walnut Crusted Salmon

Prep Time: 15 minutes.

Cook Time: 43 minutes.

Serves: 2

Ingredients:

- 10 walnuts, chopped
- 2 tablespoons hemp seeds
- Salt and black pepper, to taste
- 1 lemon, halved
- Olive oil, to cook
- 2 (6-ounce) pieces of wild salmon
- 2 tablespoons ghee
- 1 head of broccoli, florets
- 1 small cauliflower head, riced
- 1 cup kimchi, chopped

Preparation:

1. At 275 degrees F, preheat your oven.
2. Mix black pepper, salt, hemp seeds and walnuts in a small bowl.
3. Place salmon on a parchment paper sheet place in a baking sheet and drizzle oil and lemon juice on top.
4. Add walnut mixture on top of salmon and press it gently.
5. Bake this salmon for 20 minutes in the oven.
6. Sauté broccoli with 1 tbs ghee in a large skillet for 10 minutes.
7. Add lemon juice, black pepper and salt to season the broccoli.
8. Transfer this broccoli to a bowl then add 1 tablespoon ghee and cauliflower to the same skillet.
9. Sauté for 10 minutes then add kimchi and cook for 3 minutes.
10. Serve the salmon with broccoli and cauliflower rice.

Serving Suggestion: Serve the salmon with roasted veggies.

Variation Tip: Replace salmon with the cod of halibut if needed.

Nutritional Information Per Serving:

Calories 284 | Fat 25g |Sodium 460mg | Carbs 16g | Fiber 0.4g | Sugar 2g | Protein 26g

Hoisin Glazed Salmon

Prep Time: 15 minutes.

Cook Time: 30 minutes.

Serves: 2

Ingredients:

- ½ cup soy sauce
- ½ cup water
- 1/4 cup hoisin sauce
- 3 garlic cloves
- 1 (1-inch piece) fresh ginger
- 2 tablespoons honey
- 2 limes
- 1 lb. salmon
- 1 tablespoon sesame oil
- Sesame seeds for topping

Preparation:

1. Blend lime juice, honey, ginger, garlic, hoisin, water, and soy sauce in a blender.
2. Cook this sauce in a skillet over medium heat until thickens.
3. At 350 degrees F, preheat your oven.
4. Cut the salmon fillets in four pieces and rub them with sesame oil.
5. Place these salmon pieces in a baking dish.
6. Pour the ½ of the prepared sauce on top and bake for 15 minutes.
7. Flip, pour the remaining sauce on top and bake for 15 minutes.
8. Garnish with sesame seeds on top.
9. Serve warm.

Serving Suggestion: Serve the salmon with fresh cucumber and couscous salad.

Variation Tip: Add pork rinds on top of salmon before cooking.

Nutritional Information Per Serving:

Calories 352 | Fat 2.4g |Sodium 216mg | Carbs 16g | Fiber 2.3g | Sugar 1.2g | Protein 27g

Wild Alaska Salmon and Smashed Cucumber

Prep Time: 15 minutes.

Cook Time: 40 minutes.

Serves: 4

Ingredients:

- 2 cups farro
- Juice of 2 lemons
- 2 tablespoons Dijon mustard
- 1 garlic clove, minced
- ⅓ cup 2 tablespoons olive oil
- Salt and black pepper, to taste
- 1 European cucumber, diced
- ¼ cup seasoned rice vinegar
- ¼ cup parsley, chopped
- ¼ cup mint, chopped
- ¼ cup fresh dill, chopped
- 4 (6-ounce) wild Alaska salmon fillets

Preparation:

1. Boil farro in salted water in a saucepan and cook for 30 minutes on a simmer then drain.
2. Mix the cooked farro with lemon juice, black pepper, salt, 1/3 cup olive oil, garlic and mustard in a medium bowl.
3. Mash the cucumber chunks in a bowl with a fork.
4. Stir in parsley, black pepper, salt, rice vinegar, dill, mint and parsley then mix well.
5. Add rest of the 2 tablespoons olive oil to a suitable skillet.
6. Over medium heat, sear the salmon in this oil for 5 minutes per side.
7. Season this salmon with black pepper and salt.
8. Serve this salmon with farro and cucumber salad.

Serving Suggestion: Serve the bowls with fresh herbs on top and a bowl of steamed rice.

Variation Tip: Use honey or maple syrup to season the fish.

Nutritional Information Per Serving:

Calories 388 | Fat 8g |Sodium 611mg | Carbs 8g | Fiber 0g | Sugar 4g | Protein 13g

Garlic Shrimp and Tomato Rice

Prep Time: 15 minutes.

Cook Time: 61 minutes.

Serves: 4

Ingredients:

- 14 ounces shrimp, uncooked, peeled, and deveined
- 15 Campari tomatoes, chopped
- ½ red onion, diced
- 3 garlic cloves, diced
- 1 tablespoon olive oil
- 2 tablespoons tomato paste
- ¼ cup feta cheese, crumbled
- 1 teaspoon red pepper flake
- ¾ cup jasmine rice
- ½ tablespoon unsalted butter
- 1½ cups water
- 3 tablespoons fresh parsley

Preparation:

1. Boil rice with water in a saucepan and cook on a simmer for 20 minutes.
2. Remove from the heat and leave the rice for 20 minutes.
3. Sauté onion and garlic with oil in a suitable pan for 3 minutes.
4. Stir in tomatoes and cook for 10 minutes.
5. Add red pepper flakes and tomato paste then cook for 3 minutes.
6. Stir in shrimp and cook for 3-5 minutes.
7. Add butter and parsley to the cooked rice.
8. Serve the rice with the shrimp mixture.

Serving Suggestion: Serve the shrimp and rice with kale salad.

Variation Tip: Add chopped veggies to the sauce.

Nutritional Information Per Serving:

Calories 301 | Fat 16g |Sodium 412mg | Carbs 32g | Fiber 0.2g | Sugar 1g | Protein 28.2g

Halibut with Sweet Pea Puree

Prep Time: 15 minutes.

Cook Time: 36 minutes.

Serves: 2

Ingredients:

- 1 cup water
- ½ cup jasmine rice
- 2 (6 oz) Halibut fillets
- ¼ teaspoons salt
- ½ teaspoon black pepper
- 2 cups frozen green peas
- 4 cups water
- ½ fresh lemon, juiced
- 2 tablespoons olive oil
- 2 radishes, sliced
- 1 teaspoon fresh dill
- 1 tablespoon microgreens

Preparation:

1. Boil 1 cup water and rice in a small stockpot for 20 minutes then remove from the heat.
2. Leave the cooked rice for 10 minutes.
3. Rub the halibut with black pepper and salt.
4. Add green peas to 4 cups of water in a saucepan for 6 minutes then strain.
5. Blend cooked peas with black pepper, salt, lemon juice and ¼ cup water.
6. Set a skillet with oil over medium heat and sear the halibut for 5 minutes per side until golden brown.
7. Spoon the peas mixture in the serving plate and top it with halibut.
8. Garnish with radishes, dill and microgreens.
9. Serve warm with the rice on the side.

Serving Suggestion: Serve the halibut with white rice or vegetable chow Mein.

Variation Tip: Wrap the halibut with bacon before cooking for more taste.

Nutritional Information Per Serving:

Calories 231 | Fat 20.1g |Sodium 364mg | Carbs 30g | Fiber 1g | Sugar 1.4g | Protein 15g

Swordfish with Roasted Beets

Prep Time: 15 minutes.

Cook Time: 63 minutes.

Serves: 2

Ingredients:

Beets

- 1¼ cup beet, peeled and cubed
- ½ tablespoon olive oil
- ¼ teaspoons black pepper
- 1 dash salt
- ¼ cup sweet pea greens
- 1 teaspoon goat cheese

Parsnip puree

- 1 cup parsnip, diced
- 3 tablespoons almond milk
- ½ tablespoon unsalted butter

Swordfish

- 6 ½ ounces swordfish
- ¼ tablespoons olive oil
- 1 teaspoon lemon pepper seasoning

Preparation:

1. At 400 degrees F, preheat your oven.
2. Layer a baking sheet with a foil sheet.
3. Toss beets with black pepper, salt and olive oil in a baking sheet, lined with foil sheet.
4. Roast these beets for 40 minutes in the oven and toss once cooked halfway through.
5. Boil parsnip with 3 cups water in a medium pot and cook for 15 minutes until soft then drain.
6. Rub the swordfish with lemon pepper seasoning and oil.
7. Set a skillet over low-medium heat then sear the swordfish for 4 minutes per side.
8. Blend the cooked parsnip with almond milk and butter in a blender for 2 minutes.
9. Spread this puree in a serving plate.
10. Set the swordfish on top and top it with peas and beets.

11. Garnish with goat cheese and serve.

Serving Suggestion: Serve the swordfish with avocado salad.

Variation Tip: Add sweet paprika to season the fish for a tangy taste.

Nutritional Information Per Serving:

Calories 440 | Fat 14g |Sodium 220mg | Carbs 22g | Fiber 0.2g | Sugar 1g | Protein 37g

Lemon Risotto and Shrimp

Prep Time: 15 minutes.

Cook Time: 29 minutes.

Serves: 4

Ingredients:

- 16 ounces shrimp, uncooked
- ½ teaspoon cayenne pepper
- ½ teaspoon lemon pepper seasoning
- ½ teaspoon garlic powder
- 2 lemons juiced
- 1 teaspoon olive oil
- 5 ounces yellow onion, diced
- 1 cup arborio rice
- 6 cups water
- 1 teaspoon chicken base
- 1 tablespoon unsalted butter
- 1 ounce Dubliner cheese, shredded
- 2 tablespoons parsley, chopped

Preparation:

1. Mix shrimp with lemon juice, garlic powder, lemon pepper, and cayenne pepper in a large bowl.
2. Cover and refrigerate the shrimp for 15 minutes.
3. At 400 degrees F, preheat your oven.
4. Sauté onions with oil in a skillet for 5 minutes.
5. Stir in rice and sauté for 1 minute.
6. Add chicken base and water then cook until rice is cooked well and water is reduced.
7. Layer a baking sheet lined with foil and spread the shrimp on it.
8. Bake the shrimp for 8 minutes in the oven.
9. Divide the risotto in serving bowls and top it with shrimp.
10. Garnish with parsley and serve warm.

Serving Suggestion: Serve the shrimp bowl with kale salad.

Variation Tip: Add chopped mushrooms to the risotto.

Nutritional Information Per Serving:

Calories 380 | Fat 8g |Sodium 339mg | Carbs 33g | Fiber 1g | Sugar 2g | Protein 21g

Pesto Shrimp with Snow Peas

Prep Time: 15 minutes.

Cook Time: 46 minutes.

Serves: 8

Ingredients:

- 2 cups water
- 1 cup jasmine rice
- 24 ounces shrimp, peeled
- ½ lemon, juiced
- 2 tablespoons basil pesto
- ½ teaspoon black pepper
- ½ teaspoon garlic powder
- 3 cloves fresh garlic, diced
- ½ cup red onion, sliced
- 2 tablespoons basil pesto
- ¼ cup water
- 2 cup asparagus, chopped
- 2 cup snow peas, ends trimmed

- ¼ cup serrano pepper, sliced
- ¼ cup scallions, sliced
- 1 teaspoon white sesame seeds
- ¼ cup radish, cut into matchsticks

Preparation:

1. Boil rice with 2 cups water in a saucepan and cover to cook on a simmer for 20 minutes then remove from the heat.
2. Mix shrimp with garlic powder, black pepper, 2 tablespoons basil pesto and juice from ½ lemon in a bowl.
3. Cover and refrigerate the shrimp for 15 minutes.
4. Sauté shrimp with oil in a skillet for 4 minutes.
5. Stir in garlic, onions, 2 tablespoons pesto and ¼ cup water and cook for 2 minutes.
6. Stir in serrano peppers, snow peas and asparagus and cook for 2 minutes.
7. Cover and cook for 3 minutes.
8. Add scallion, and black pepper to the rice.
9. Serve the rice with shrimp mixture and garnish with sesame seeds and radish.

Serving Suggestion: Serve the shrimp with steaming white rice.

Variation Tip: Add 1 tablespoon lemon juice to the seasoning.

Nutritional Information Per Serving:

Calories 361 | Fat 16g |Sodium 189mg | Carbs 19.3g | Fiber 0.3g | Sugar 18.2g | Protein 33.3g

Zucchini Noodles and Lemon Shrimp

Prep Time: 15 minutes.

Cook Time: 10 minutes.

Serves: 4

Ingredients:

- 4 medium zucchinis, spiralized
- 18 ounces shrimp, peeled and deveined
- 1 lemon, juiced
- 1 teaspoon black pepper
- 1 teaspoon garlic powder
- ¼ teaspoons old bay seasoning
- ½ tablespoon unsalted butter
- ¼ teaspoons salt
- 1 tablespoon Italian parsley

Preparation:

1. Toss shrimp with garlic, black pepper, old bay and juice from ½ lemon in a bowl.
2. Mix the spiralized zucchini with remaining lemon juice and salt in a bowl.
3. Sauté shrimp with its marinade in a skillet for 5 minutes.
4. Stir in butter, zucchini noodles, garlic powder and pepper.
5. Cover and cook for 5 minutes then toss well.
6. Garnish with lemon wedge and fresh parsley.
7. Enjoy.

Serving Suggestion: Serve the noodles with a quinoa salad

Variation Tip: Add dried herbs for seasoning.

Nutritional Information Per Serving:

Calories 405 | Fat 20g | Sodium 941mg | Carbs 16.1g | Fiber 0.9g | Sugar 0.9g | Protein 45.2g

Beef, Pork and Lamb

Skillet Pepper Steak

Prep Time: 15 minutes.

Cook Time: 11 minutes.

Serves: 4

Ingredients:

- 12 ounces top round beef, sliced
- Salt and black pepper, to taste
- 2 tablespoons peanut oil
- 1 tablespoon soy sauce
- 1 tablespoon rice wine vinegar
- 1½ teaspoon crushed red-pepper flakes
- 1 red bell pepper, sliced
- 1 yellow bell pepper, sliced
- 1 green bell pepper, sliced
- 1 orange bell pepper, sliced
- 3 garlic cloves, minced
- 1 bunch scallions, sliced
- Sesame seeds, for finishing

Preparation:

1. Rub the steak with black pepper and salt.
2. Set a large skillet over medium high heat with 1 tablespoon oil.
3. Sear the steak for 2 minutes per side then transfer to a plate.
4. Mix soy sauce, red pepper flakes, vinegar and rice vinegar.
5. Pour this mixture over the steak.
6. Sauté pepper with 1 tablespoon oil the same skillet for 4 minutes.
7. Make a space at the center and add the steak.
8. Cook for 2 minutes then add garlic and cook for 1 minute.
9. Garnish with sesame seeds and serve warm.

Serving Suggestion: Serve the steak with a fresh crouton salad.

Variation Tip: Add a drizzle of cheese on top of the steak.

Nutritional Information Per Serving:

Calories 345 | Fat 7.9g |Sodium 581mg | Carbs 10g | Fiber 2.6g | Sugar 0.1g | Protein 42.5g

Pistachio Pork Tenderloin with Escarole Salad

Prep Time: 15 minutes.

Cook Time: 30 minutes.

Serves: 2

Ingredients:

Pork Tenderloin

- 1 cup unsalted shelled pistachios
- 1 garlic clove
- 1 tablespoon fresh rosemary leaves
- Pinch of cayenne pepper
- 1½ lbs. pork tenderloin
- Salt and black pepper, to taste

Salad

- 1 head escarole, torn into bite-size pieces
- 1 apple, sliced
- Juice of 1 lemon
- 2 tablespoons white wine vinegar
- 2 teaspoons Dijon mustard
- ¼ cup olive oil
- Salt and black pepper, to taste

Preparation:

1. At 375 degrees F, preheat your oven.
2. Layer a baking sheet with cooking spray.
3. Blend cayenne, rosemary, garlic and pistachios in a blender.
4. Spread this mixture over a parchment paper.
5. Rub the pork with black pepper and salt then coat with the pistachio's mixture.
6. Place the coated pork in the baking sheet.
7. Bake for 25-30 minutes in oven.
8. Meanwhile, toss all the escarole salad ingredients in a bowl.
9. Slice the pork and serve it with the salad.
10. Enjoy.

Serving Suggestion: Serve the pork with toasted bread slices.

Variation Tip: Add other chopped nuts to coat the pork tenderloin,

Nutritional Information Per Serving:

Calories 319 | Fat 13g | Sodium 432mg | Carbs 9.1g | Fiber 3g | Sugar 1g | Protein 33g

BBQ Baked Pork Chops

Prep Time: 15 minutes.

Cook Time: 56 minutes.

Serves: 4

Ingredients:

- ½ cup parmesan cheese, grated
- 1 ½ teaspoon garlic powder
- 1 tablespoon dried parsley
- 1 teaspoon dried thyme
- 1 teaspoon paprika
- ¾ teaspoons salt
- ½ teaspoon black pepper
- ½ teaspoon onion powder
- ¼ teaspoons chili powder
- 1/8 teaspoons oregano
- 1 tablespoon avocado oil
- 4 pork chops

Preparation:

1. At 350 degrees F, preheat your oven.
2. Layer a suitable baking dish with cooking spray.
3. Mix spices with parmesan cheese in a shallow bowl.
4. Set a skillet with avocado oil over medium heat.
5. Coat the pork chops with parmesan cheese and sear for 3 minutes per side until golden brown.
6. Transfer the chops to the baking dish and pour the barbecue sauce on top.
7. Bake the chops for 50 minutes in the oven.
8. Serve warm.

Serving Suggestion: Serve the chops with roasted veggies on the side.

Variation Tip: Add sweet paprika for more taste.

Nutritional Information Per Serving:

Calories 334 | Fat 16g |Sodium 462mg | Carbs 31g | Fiber 0.4g | Sugar 3g | Protein 35.3g

Pork Chops & Broccoli

Prep Time: 15 minutes.

Cook Time: 25 minutes.

Serves: 8

Ingredients:

- 8 thin boneless pork chops
- 4 cups fresh broccoli, chopped
- 2 tablespoons olive oil
- 1 tablespoon butter
- ½ cup parmesan cheese, grated
- ¾ cup mozzarella cheese, grated
- 6 garlic cloves, minced
- 1 tablespoon parsley
- ¾ teaspoons thyme
- ½ teaspoon pink salt
- ¼ teaspoons black pepper
- 1 teaspoon parsley

Preparation:

1. At 400 degrees F, preheat your oven.
2. Layer a baking sheet with parchment paper.
3. Mix spices, parmesan cheese, oil and butter in a bowl.
4. Coat the pork chops with this mixture.
5. Place the coated pork in a baking sheet and drizzle 1/3 of the remaining parmesan cheese mixture on top.
6. Toss the broccoli with remaining spice mixture in a bowl.
7. Spread the broccoli around the pork chops and cover with a foil sheet.
8. Bake the chops for 5 minutes then uncover and bake again for 5 minutes.
9. Add mozzarella cheese on top then bake for 12 minutes.
10. Broil the pork for 3 minutes then garnish with parsley.
11. Serve warm.

Serving Suggestion: Serve the pork chops with mashed potatoes.

Variation Tip: Use BBQ sauce to season the pork chops for the change of taste.

Nutritional Information Per Serving:

Calories 305 | Fat 25g |Sodium 532mg | Carbs 2.3g | Fiber 0.4g | Sugar 2g | Protein 18.3g

Beef Chilli

Prep Time: 15 minutes.

Cook Time: 1 hr. 30 minutes.

Serves: 6

Ingredients:

- 9 ounces onions. chopped
- 2 ounces peppers, chopped
- 3 red chilis, chopped
- 2 x 14 ounces tins chopped tomatoes
- 4 x 14 ounces tins kidney beans
- 28 ounces lean steak mince
- 1 x ½ ounces sachet deep south seasoning

Preparation:

1. Mix onions, peppers, red chilies, tomatoes, kidney beans, minced and south seasoning in a large saucepan.
2. Cook this beef Chilli on low heat for 1 ½ hours while mixing every 30 minutes.
3. Serve warm.

Serving Suggestion: Serve the beef chili with toasted bread slices.

Variation Tip: Add crumbled bacon to the mixture.

Nutritional Information Per Serving:

Calories 325 | Fat 16g |Sodium 431mg | Carbs 22g | Fiber 1.2g | Sugar 4g | Protein 23g

Pork Shoulder

Prep Time: 15 minutes.

Cook Time: 10 hrs. 11 minutes.

Serves: 6

Ingredients:

- 3 lbs. boneless pork shoulder
- 1 tablespoon olive oil
- 1 large yellow onion, sliced
- 10 garlic cloves, sliced
- 1 teaspoon cumin
- 1 teaspoon paprika
- ¼ cup tomato paste
- ¼ cup coconut aminos
- Salt, to taste
- Black pepper, to taste

Preparation:

1. Pat dry the pork with paper towel.
2. Set a skillet with olive oil over medium high heat and sear the pork for 4 minutes per side then transfer to a plate.
3. Reduce the skillet's heat and add onion.
4. Sauté for 2 minutes then add paprika, garlic and cumin.
5. Sauté for 30 seconds and then transfer this mixture to a slow cooker.
6. Add pork shoulder and the rest of the ingredients.
7. Cover and cook the pork for 10 hours on low setting.
8. Shred the cooked pork with a fork.
9. Serve warm.

Serving Suggestion: Serve this pork with rice, pasta, or spaghetti.

Variation Tip: Add some chopped bell pepper to the slow cooker.

Nutritional Information Per Serving:

Calories 268 | Fat 7g |Sodium 411mg | Carbs 5g | Fiber 1g | Sugar 2g | Protein 21g

Chipotle Baked Pork Chops

Prep Time: 15 minutes.

Cook Time: 31 minutes.

Serves: 2

Ingredients:

Cinnamon Chipotle Rub

- 1 tablespoon coconut sugar
- 1 teaspoon ground chili powder
- ½ teaspoon cinnamon
- ¼ teaspoons garlic powder
- ¼ teaspoons onion powder
- ¼ teaspoons smoked paprika
- 1 pinch of dried oregano
- ½ teaspoon sea salt
- ¼ teaspoons ground black pepper

Pan:

- 2 large parsnips, cut into slices
- 2 large carrots, cut into slices
- 3 tablespoons olive oil
- 1 ½ lbs boneless pork chops
- Parsley to garnish
- Lemon slices, to garnish
- Red Chili pepper flakes, to garnish

Preparation:

1. Mix the ingredients for cinnamon chipotle rub in a small bowl.
2. At 400 degrees F, preheat your oven.
3. Toss carrots and parsnips with 2 tablespoons oil and 2 teaspoons cinnamon chipotle rubs in a bowl.
4. Spread the veggies in a baking sheet and roast for 15 minutes.
5. Rub the remaining chipotle rub and 1 tablespoon olive oil over the pork chops.
6. Sear the pork chops in the skillet for 4 minutes per side.
7. Transfer the chops to the baking sheet.
8. Return this baking sheet to the oven and bake for 8 minutes at 400 degrees F.

9. Garnish with lemon slices, red pepper flakes and parsley.

10. Serve warm.

Serving Suggestion: Serve the chops with sweet potato mash.

Variation Tip: Add cheese on top of the chops and then bake.

Nutritional Information Per Serving:

Calories 425 | Fat 15g |Sodium 345mg | Carbs 12.3g | Fiber 1.4g | Sugar 3g | Protein 23.3g

Beef Stew

Prep Time: 15 minutes.

Cook Time: 43 minutes.

Serves: 4

Ingredients:

- 2 lbs. beef chuck roast, diced
- 1 tablespoon olive oil
- 1 ½ cups onion, diced
- 4 carrots, cut into slices
- 3 garlic cloves, minced
- 1 lb gold potatoes, diced
- 2 cups beef broth
- ¼ cup tomato paste
- 2 tablespoons balsamic vinegar
- 1 teaspoon dried rosemary
- ½ teaspoon salt
- 2 tablespoons cornstarch
- 1 cup frozen peas

Preparation:

1. Add cubed beef and oil to an Instant Pot and cook on Sauté mode for 5 minutes.
2. Stir in garlic, carrots and onion then sauté for 5 minutes.
3. Add salt, rosemary, balsamic vinegar, tomato paste, beef broth and potatoes.
4. Cover the pressure-cooking lid and cook on High Pressure for 30 minutes
5. Release the pressure naturally and remove the lid.
6. Mix cornstarch with 2 tablespoons cold water in a small bowl.
7. Add this mixture and peas to the stew and cook on Sauté mode for 3 minutes with occasional stirring.
8. Serve warm.

Serving Suggestion: Serve the stew with boiled rice

Variation Tip: Dust the beef with flour before cooking for more texture.

Nutritional Information Per Serving:

Calories 391 | Fat 5g |Sodium 88mg | Carbs 3g | Fiber 0g | Sugar 0g | Protein 17g

Spaghetti & Meatballs

Prep Time: 15 minutes.

Cook Time: 40 minutes.

Serves: 4

Ingredients:

- 1-lb. lean ground beef
- 2 eggs
- 1 large carrot, grated
- 3 cups baby spinach, chopped
- 1 teaspoon garlic salt
- 1/4 teaspoon black pepper
- 2 tablespoons oregano
- 1 cup breadcrumbs
- 1 (25 ounce) jar pasta sauce
- 1 (7 ounce) pack black bean spaghetti

Preparation:

1. At 375 degrees F, preheat your oven.
2. Mix beef with breadcrumbs, carrots, eggs, oregano, black pepper, spinach, and garlic salt in a bowl.
3. Make 2 inches balls out of this mixture and place them in a baking sheet lined with parchment paper.
4. Bake the beef meatballs in the oven for 30 minutes.
5. Meanwhile, boil the pasta in salted water as per the package's instructions then drain.
6. Warm the pasta sauce in a bowl by heating in the microwave.
7. Divide the pasta in the serving plates and top it with meatballs, pasta sauce and parmesan cheese.
8. Serve warm.

Serving Suggestion: Serve the spaghetti with roasted broccoli.

Variation Tip: Serve the meatballs with spaghetti on top of lettuce bed.

Nutritional Information Per Serving:

Calories 276 | Fat 21g |Sodium 476mg | Carbs 22g | Fiber 3g | Sugar 4g | Protein 20g

Sesame Beef

Prep Time: 15 minutes.

Cook Time: 8 hours

Serves: 6

Ingredients:

- 3 lbs. beef roast
- ½ cup coconut aminos
- 1 cup water

Dipping sauce:

- 2 tablespoons sesame oil
- 1 tablespoon sesame seeds
- 2 garlic cloves, peeled and minced
- ¼ cup coconut aminos

Preparation:

1. Add beef, water and ½ cup coconut aminos to a slow cooker.
2. Cover and cook the beef for 8 hours on low heat.
3. Once done, remove the beef from the slow cooker and slice.
4. Mix all the dipping sauce ingredients in a bowl.
5. Serve the beef slices with the dipping sauce.
6. Enjoy.

Serving Suggestion: Serve the beef with kale quinoa salad on the side.

Variation Tip: Cook the beef with chopped bell pepper in the slow cooker.

Nutritional Information Per Serving:

Calories 374 | Fat 5g |Sodium 132mg | Carbs 4g | Fiber 0g | Sugar 0g | Protein 46g

Vegetarian Mains

Veggie Burgers

Prep Time: 15 minutes.

Cook Time: 12 minutes.

Serves: 4

Ingredients:

- 1/3 cup rolled oats
- 1 (14-ounce) can chickpeas, drained and rinsed
- 2 teaspoons coconut aminos
- 2 teaspoons lime juice
- 2 teaspoons sesame oil
- 2 teaspoons garlic, minced
- 2 teaspoons powdered ginger
- 2 tablespoons peanut butter
- 2 tablespoons cilantro, chopped

Preparation:

1. Blend oats with cilantro, peanut butter, ginger, garlic, sesame oil, lime juice, chickpeas and coconut aminos in a blender.
2. Set a skillet over medium heat and grease it with cooking spray.
3. Make 4 equal sized patties out of this mixture and sear them for 6 minutes per side.
4. Serve warm.

Serving Suggestion: Serve the burgers with whole wheat buns.

Variation Tip: Add sliced tomatoes, lettuce and onion on top of burgers before serving.

Nutritional Information Per Serving:

Calories 251 | Fat 11g |Sodium 515mg | Carbs 32g | Fiber 0.1g | Sugar 18.2g | Protein 11g

Pesto Omelet

Prep Time: 15 minutes.

Cook Time: 19 minutes.

Serves: 4

Ingredients:

- ½ cup basil leaves
- ½ cup kale, destemmed
- 2 brazil nuts
- 2 teaspoons nutritional yeast
- 2 teaspoons chives
- 2 teaspoons lemon juice
- ½ teaspoon salt, divided
- Olive oil in a spray container
- ½ cup sweet potatoes, chopped
- ¼ cup of cherry tomatoes, quartered
- ¼ cup bell pepper, chopped
- 4 eggs

Preparation:

1. Blend kale, basil, brazil nuts, yeast, chives, 2 teaspoons water, 1/8 teaspoons salt and lemon juice in a blender.
2. Grease an 8-inch pan with olive oil and sauté potatoes with a pinch of salt for 10 minutes.
3. Beat 4 eggs with a splash of water and 1/8 teaspoons salt in a bowl.
4. Add 1 pinch of salt, bell pepper and cherry tomatoes to the sweet potatoes.
5. Cook for 5 minutes then transfer to a plate.
6. Add a spritz of oil to the same pan and pour in eggs.
7. Cook for 2 minutes then cover and cook for 2 minutes.
8. Add a dollop of pest, and veggie mixture on top.
9. Fold the omelet over the veggies and serve warm.

Serving Suggestion: Serve the omelet with toasted bread.

Variation Tip: Add butter to the omelet before serving.

Nutritional Information Per Serving:

Calories 305 | Fat 22.7g |Sodium 227mg | Carbs 6.1g | Fiber 1.4g | Sugar 0.9g | Protein 45.2g

Sesame Baked Tofu

Prep Time: 15 minutes.

Cook Time: 20 minutes.

Serves: 4

Ingredients:

- 1 package extra firm tofu
- 1/4 cup soy sauce
- 1/4 cup lemon juice
- 1 tablespoon sesame oil
- 1 tablespoon raw honey
- 2 tablespoons rice wine vinegar
- 1 teaspoon fresh ginger root, grated
- 1 teaspoon Sriracha
- A sprinkle of sesame seeds
- 2 sprigs of cilantro

Preparation:

1. At 400 degrees F, preheat your oven.
2. Pat dry the tofu and cut into cubes.
3. Mix sriracha sauce with ginger, vinegar, honey, sesame oil, lemon juice and soy sauce in a bowl.
4. Stir in tofu and mix well to coat.
5. Cover and refrigerate the tofu for 1 hour.
6. Transfer the tofu to a baking sheet and bake for 20 minutes and stir after 10 minutes.
7. Garnish with sesame seeds and cilantro.
8. Serve warm.

Serving Suggestion: Serve the tofu with boiled peas, carrots, and potatoes on the side.

Variation Tip: Add butter to the tofu for more taste.

Nutritional Information Per Serving:

Calories 245 | Fat 6g |Sodium 272mg | Carbs 11g | Fiber 0.2g | Sugar 0.1g | Protein 22.5g

Butter Beans and Olives

Prep Time: 15 minutes.

Cook Time: 23 minutes.

Serves: 4

Ingredients:

- 1 teaspoon olive oil
- 4 garlic cloves, minced
- 1 (15-oz) can butter beans
- 1 (15-oz) can diced tomatoes
- 1/8 cup oil cured olives, chopped
- Dried basil, to taste
- 1 teaspoon red pepper flakes

Preparation:

1. Sauté garlic with olive oil in a saucepan for 3 minutes.
2. Stir in beans, spices and tomatoes then cook to a boil.
3. Reduce its heat and cook on a simmer for 20 minutes.
4. Serve warm.

Serving Suggestion: Serve the sauce with sautéed green beans and rice

Variation Tip: Add a drizzle of cheese on top.

Nutritional Information Per Serving:

Calories 295 | Fat 9.5g |Sodium 655mg | Carbs 23.4g | Fiber 0.4g | Sugar 0.4g | Protein 18.3g

Cauliflower Fried Rice

Prep Time: 15 minutes.

Cook Time: 15 minutes.

Serves: 4

Ingredients:

- 1 teaspoon sesame oil
- 3 garlic cloves, minced
- 4 carrots, peeled and diced
- 1 teaspoon red pepper flakes, to taste
- 1 ½ heads of cauliflower, riced
- 4 green onions, diced
- 1 cup frozen green peas
- 1 cup frozen corn
- 3 tablespoons soy sauce
- Salt and black pepper, to taste

Preparation:

1. Sauté garlic with sesame oil in a wok over medium heat for 2 minutes.
2. Stir in carrots and cook for 3 minutes.
3. Add soy sauce, corn, peas, cauliflower rice and red pepper flakes.
4. Cook for 10 minutes on and serve warm.

Serving Suggestion: Serve the rice with fresh greens and mashed potatoes.

Variation Tip: Add a drizzle of herbs on top of the rice.

Nutritional Information Per Serving:

Calories 201 | Fat 5g |Sodium 340mg | Carbs 14.7g | Fiber 1.2g | Sugar 1.3g | Protein 5.3g

Red Cauliflower Rice

Prep Time: 15 minutes.

Cook Time: 17 minutes.

Serves: 4

Ingredients:

- ½ teaspoon coconut oil
- ½ white onion, diced
- 3 garlic cloves, minced
- 1 tablespoon fresh ginger, peeled and minced
- 1 jalapeño, minced
- 5 small carrots, peeled and diced
- 2 tablespoons red curry paste
- 1 red bell pepper, diced
- 1 head of cauliflower, riced
- 1 cup green peas
- 1 cup lite coconut milk
- 2 tablespoons soy sauce
- Salt and black pepper, to taste

Preparation:

1. Sauté carrot, jalapeno, ginger, garlic and onion with oil in a saucepan for 5 minutes.
2. Stir in red curry paste, cauliflower, red pepper, soy sauce and coconut milk then cook for 10 minutes with occasional stirring.
3. Add green peas and cook for 2 minutes.
4. Garnish with cilantro and green onion,
5. Serve warm.

Serving Suggestion: Serve the rice with quinoa salad.

Variation Tip: Add crispy tofu on top.

Nutritional Information Per Serving:

Calories 148 | Fat 23g |Sodium 350mg | Carbs 8g | Fiber 6.3g | Sugar 1g | Protein 10.3g

Baked Curried Tofu

Prep Time: 15 minutes.

Cook Time: 30 minutes.

Serves: 4

Ingredients:

- 1 package organic extra-firm tofu
- 2 tablespoons soy sauce
- 1 tablespoon curry powder
- ½ teaspoon garlic powder

Preparation:

1. At 400 degrees F, preheat your oven.
2. Cut the tofu into cubes and mix with spices, tamari and soy sauce in a bowl.
3. Spread the tofu mixture in a baking pan and bake for 30 minutes.
4. Flip them once cooked halfway through.
5. Serve warm.

Serving Suggestion: Serve the tofu with caprese side on the side.

Variation Tip: Add julienned bell pepper to the tofu.

Nutritional Information Per Serving:

Calories 209 | Fat 25g |Sodium 463mg | Carbs 9.9g | Fiber 0.3g | Sugar 0.3g | Protein 8g

Red Lentil Dahl

Prep Time: 15 minutes.

Cook Time: 40 minutes.

Serves: 4

Ingredients:

- 1 tablespoon coconut oil
- 2 yellow onions, diced
- 4 medium garlic cloves, minced
- 1 tablespoon fresh ginger, peeled, minced
- 1 tablespoon curry powder
- 1 teaspoon turmeric
- ½ teaspoon coriander
- ½ teaspoon black pepper
- 1 teaspoon sea salt
- ½ teaspoon red pepper flakes
- 2 cups dry red lentils
- 1 can coconut milk
- 3 cups water
- Fresh cilantro for serving
- cooked jasmine, basmati or brown rice, for serving (optional)

Preparation:

1. Sauté ginger, garlic and onions with coconut oil in a skillet for 10 minutes.
2. Stir in water, lentils, coconut milk and spices then cook on a simmer for 30 minutes.
3. Garnish with cilantro and serve warm with rice or quinoa.
4. Enjoy.

Serving Suggestion: Serve the lentils with kale side on the side.

Variation Tip: Add more veggies of your choice to the lentils.

Nutritional Information Per Serving:

Calories 237 | Fat 20g |Sodium 719mg | Carbs 25.1g | Fiber 0.9g | Sugar 1.4g | Protein 7.8g

Chilli Sin Carne

Prep Time: 15 minutes.

Cook Time: 31 minutes.

Serves: 6

Ingredients:

- 2 tablespoons olive oil
- 3 garlic cloves, minced
- 1 large red onion, sliced
- 2 celery stalks, chopped
- 2 medium carrots, peeled and chopped
- 2 red peppers, chopped
- 1 teaspoon ground cumin
- 1 teaspoon chili powder
- Salt and pepper, to taste
- 28 ounces tinned chopped tomatoes
- 14 ounces tin of red kidney beans, drained and rinsed
- 3 ½ ounces split red lentils
- 14 ounces frozen soy mince
- 1 cup vegetable stock

Add-ins

- 1 teaspoon miso paste
- 2 tablespoons balsamic vinegar
- A handful of fresh coriander, chopped

Serve

- Cooked basmati rice
- Chopped coriander
- A squeeze of lime juice

Preparation:

1. Sauté peppers with carrots, celery, onion and garlic in a suitable pan for 5 minutes.
2. Stir in chili powder, black pepper, salt, and cumin
3. Sauté for 1 minutes then add stock, soy mince, lentils, beans and tomatoes.

4. Cook this mixture on a simmer for 25 minutes.

5. Serve warm with rice.

Serving Suggestion: Serve the chili with warmed tortilla

Variation Tip: Add paprika for more spice.

Nutritional Information Per Serving:

Calories 448 | Fat 13g |Sodium 353mg | Carbs 31g | Fiber 0.4g | Sugar 1g | Protein 9g

Cauliflower Lentil Loaf

Prep Time: 15 minutes.

Cook Time: 45 minutes.

Serves: 6

Ingredients:

- 1 cup cooked brown lentils
- 3 cups raw riced cauliflower
- 1 cup sweet onion, chopped
- 2 cups bell pepper, chopped
- 2 tb nutritional yeast
- 1 teaspoon garlic, minced
- 1 teaspoon Dijon mustard
- ½ teaspoon smoked paprika
- ½ teaspoon cumin
- ¼ teaspoons black pepper
- ¼ teaspoons chipotle powder

Ketchup glaze

- ⅓ cup unsweetened ketchup
- 1 teaspoon liquid smoke

Preparation:

1. At 400 degrees F, preheat your oven.
2. Sauté pepper and onion in a suitable skillet until soft.
3. Blend these veggies with rest of the ingredients in a food processor.
4. Layer a 9x5 inch loaf pan with parchment sheet and spread the loaf mixture in it.
5. Mix liquid smoke and ketchup then spread over the loaf.
6. Bake this lentil loaf for 45 minutes in the oven.
7. Slice and serve.

Serving Suggestion: Serve the meatloaf with cucumber salad and cauliflower rice

Variation Tip: Add dried herbs to the loaf for seasoning.

Nutritional Information Per Serving:

Calories 376 | Fat 17g | Sodium 1127mg | Carbs 24g | Fiber 1g | Sugar 3g | Protein 7g

Snacks and Sides

Strawberry Protein Balls

Prep Time: 10 minutes.

Cook Time: 0 minutes.

Serves: 6

Ingredients:

- 1 scoop vanilla protein powder
- 1/3 cup oats dry
- 1 tablespoon Jell-O Powder
- 1 teaspoon strawberry

Preparation:

1. Blend jello powder, oats, strawberry, and protein powder in a food processor.
2. Make small ball out of this mixture.
3. Serve.

Serving Suggestion: Serve the protein balls with hot chocolate.

Variation Tip: Drizzle melted chocolate on top for a rich taste.

Nutritional Information Per Serving:

Calories 44 | Fat 0.5g |Sodium 557mg | Carbs 5g | Fiber 1.8g | Sugar 1.2g | Protein 5g

Graham Cracker Snack

Prep Time: 5 minutes.

Cook Time: 0 minutes.

Serves: 2

Ingredients:

- 1 graham cracker sheet, cut in half
- 1 cup Greek yogurt
- 1 peach, sliced
- 1 tablespoon honey
- 1 dash cinnamon

Preparation:

1. Top each half of the graham cracker sheet with yogurt, peaches, honey and cinnamon.
2. Serve.

Serving Suggestion: Serve the snack with hot chocolate.

Variation Tip: Drizzle melted chocolate on top for a rich taste.

Nutritional Information Per Serving:

Calories 192 | Fat 16g |Sodium 466mg | Carbs 3.9g | Fiber 0.9g | Sugar 0.6g | Protein 8g

Chocolate Protein Balls

Prep Time: 15 minutes.

Cook Time: 0 minutes.

Serves: 6

Ingredients:

- 3 cups old fashioned rolled oats
- 2 scoops chocolate protein powder
- ½ cup peanut butter powder mixed
- ¼ cup 5 tablespoons water
- ⅓ cup honey
- 1½ tablespoon cacao nibs
- 1 tablespoon chia seeds
- ¼ cup mini chocolate chips
- ¼ teaspoons salt

Preparation:

1. Blend peanut butter powder with water in a blender until smooth.
2. Stir in rest of the ingredients and mix well.
3. Make small balls out of this mixture and place them in a baking sheet.
4. Freeze these balls for 15 minutes.
5. Serve.

Serving Suggestion: Serve the protein balls with pumpkin smoothies.

Variation Tip: Drizzle melted chocolate on top for a rich taste.

Nutritional Information Per Serving:

Calories 121 | Fat 7.4g |Sodium 356mg | Carbs 9.3g | Fiber 2.4g | Sugar 5g | Protein 7.2g

Ritz Cracker Snack

Prep Time: 5 minutes.

Cook Time: 0 minutes.

Serves: 1

Ingredients:

- 1 Ritz cracker
- 1 tablespoon peanut butter
- 4 chocolate chips

Preparation:

1. Spread peanut butter over the crackers and add 4 chocolate chips on top.
2. Serve.

Serving Suggestion: Serve the cracker with hot chocolate.

Variation Tip: Drizzle melted chocolate on top for a rich taste.

Nutritional Information Per Serving:

Calories 36 | Fat 2g |Sodium 994mg | Carbs 4g | Fiber 0.4g | Sugar 3g | Protein 1g

Cinnamon Protein Balls

Prep Time: 5 minutes.

Cook Time: 0 minutes.

Serves: 6

Ingredients:

- 1 cup quick oats
- ½ cup vanilla protein powder
- 1 tablespoon vanilla extract
- 1 tablespoon ground cinnamon
- 1 tablespoon water
- ½ cup peanut butter

Preparation:

1. Mix cinnamon, protein powder and oats in a food processor.
2. Stir in water, vanilla extract and peanut butter then mix well.
3. Make 12- 1-inch balls out of this mixture and place them in a plate.
4. Serve.

Serving Suggestion: Serve the protein balls with hot chocolate.

Variation Tip: Drizzle melted chocolate on top for a rich taste.

Nutritional Information Per Serving:

Calories 178 | Fat 21g |Sodium 146mg | Carbs 7.1g | Fiber 0.1g | Sugar 0.4g | Protein 23g

Peanut Butter Protein Balls

Prep Time: 15 minutes.

Cook Time: 0 minutes.

Serves: 5

Ingredients:

- 1/3 cup natural peanut butter
- 1/4 cup honey
- 1 scoop chocolate protein powder
- 3 tablespoons ground flaxseed
- 3 tablespoons dark chocolate chips

Preparation:

1. Mix honey, peanut butter, protein powder, flaxseed and chocolate chips in a bowl.
2. Make 10 balls out of this mixture and refrigerate for 1 hour.
3. Serve.

Serving Suggestion: Serve the protein balls with hot chocolate.

Variation Tip: Drizzle melted chocolate on top for a rich taste.

Nutritional Information Per Serving:

Calories 151 | Fat 4g |Sodium 236mg | Carbs 9.1g | Fiber 0.3g | Sugar 0.1g | Protein 36g

Edamame Dip

Prep Time: 5 minutes.

Cook Time: 0 minute.

Serves: 6

Ingredients:

- 1 ½ cup peeled edamame beans
- 1 garlic clove
- 1 tablespoon onion, chopped
- 1/4 cup plain Greek yogurt
- 1/4 cup lemon juice
- 1 teaspoon garlic salt
- 1 teaspoon salt
- 2 teaspoons olive oil
- 1/4 cup water

Preparation:

1. Blend edamame with salt, garlic salt, lemon juice, water, yogurt, onion and garlic in a blender until smooth.
2. Pour in olive oil and blend for 30 seconds.
3. Serve.

Serving Suggestion: Serve the dip with kale chips

Variation Tip: Add blanched spinach to the dip.

Nutritional Information Per Serving:

Calories 135 | Fat 7g |Sodium 316mg | Carbs 8g | Fiber 0.3g | Sugar 0.3g | Protein 9g

Avocado Toast

Prep Time: 5 minutes.

Cook Time: 0 minutes.

Serves: 2

Ingredients:

- 2 ounces avocado flesh
- 1 egg, boiled, peeled and sliced
- 2 sourdough bread slices, toasted
- 1 tablespoon nutritional yeast
- 1 tablespoon salsa
- 1/4 lemon, juiced
- Salt, to taste
- Garlic powder, to serve
- Bean sprouts, to serve

Preparation:

1. Mash avocado in a bowl and add lemon juice, salsa, and yeast then mix well.
2. Stir in garlic and salt then mix again.
3. Spread this mash over the bread toasted bread.
4. Add egg slices and sprouts on top.
5. Serve.

Serving Suggestion: Serve the toasts with roasted broccoli florets.

Variation Tip: Drizzle garlic butter on top before serving.

Nutritional Information Per Serving:

Calories 269 | Fat 13g |Sodium 634mg | Carbs 18 g | Fiber 1.4g | Sugar 1g | Protein 12g

Baked Chicken Wings

Prep Time: 15 minutes.

Cook Time: 50 minutes.

Serves: 8

Ingredients:

- 2 lbs. chicken wings
- 1 tablespoon garlic powder
- 1 tablespoon paprika or smoked paprika
- 1 tablespoon dried oregano
- 1 tablespoon salt
- 1 teaspoon dried chili flakes

Sauce

- 1 tablespoon coconut oil
- 1 tablespoon apple cider vinegar
- 12 ounces hot sauce

Preparation:

1. At 350 degrees F, preheat your oven.
2. Mix chicken wings with garlic powder, and the rest of the ingredients in a bowl.
3. Spread these chicken wings in a baking sheet, lined with foil sheet.
4. Bake the wings for 45 minutes in the preheated oven.
5. Mix coconut oil, apple cider vinegar and hot sauce in a saucepan and cook on low heat for 5 minutes.
6. Serve the wings with this sauce.

Serving Suggestion: Serve the wings with cream cheese dip and potato salad.

Variation Tip: Add garlic salt to the sauce for more taste.

Nutritional Information Per Serving:

Calories 251 | Fat 17g |Sodium 723mg | Carbs 11g | Fiber 2.5g | Sugar 2g | Protein 27.3g

Buffalo Chicken Dip

Prep Time: 15 minutes.

Cook Time: 8 minutes.

Serves: 8

Ingredients:

- 16 ounces shredded chicken
- 1 cup cottage cheese
- ½ cup Hot wing sauce
- ½ cup Greek yogurt
- 1 tablespoon ranch seasoning mix
- 1/4 cup cheddar cheese, shredded

Preparation:

1. At 425 degrees F, preheat your oven.
2. Grease a baking dish with cooking spray.
3. Mix ranch seasoning with yogurt in a bowl.
4. Stir in shredded chicken, wing sauce and cottage cheese.
5. Spread this chicken mixture in the baking dish and drizzle cheddar cheese on top.
6. Bake this dip for 8 minutes in the preheated oven.
7. Serve.

Serving Suggestion: Serve the dip with crackers.

Variation Tip: Add olives or sliced mushrooms to the dip.

Nutritional Information Per Serving:

Calories 246 | Fat 15g |Sodium 220mg | Carbs 40.3g | Fiber 2.4g | Sugar 1.2g | Protein 12.4g

Drinks and Beverages

Limeade

Prep Time: 5 minutes.

Cook Time: 0 minutes.

Serves: 2

Ingredients:

- 32 ounces ice water
- juice of 1 lime
- ½ squirt liquid stevia

Preparation:

1. Mix stevia, lime juice and ice water in a jug.
2. Serve.

Serving Suggestion: Serve the drink with lemon zest on top.

Variation Tip: Add some honey to the drink.

Nutritional Information Per Serving:

Calories 88 | Fat 24g |Sodium 620mg | Carbs 8.3g | Fiber 2.4g | Sugar 1.2g | Protein 5.4g

Pina Colada Smoothie

Prep Time: 5 minutes.

Cook Time: 0 minutes.

Serves: 2

Ingredients:

- ½ cup pineapple chunks
- 1 banana fresh
- 1 cup coconut milk
- ½ teaspoon vanilla protein powder
- ice if pineapple not frozen

Preparation:

1. Blend coconut milk with pineapple, protein powder, and banana in a blender.
2. Serve with ice and pineapple chunks in the glass.

Serving Suggestion: Serve the smoothie with shredded coconut on top.

Variation Tip: Add coconut cream to the smoothie.

Nutritional Information Per Serving:

Calories 93 | Fat 3g |Sodium 510mg | Carbs 12g | Fiber 3g | Sugar 4g | Protein 4g

Protein Orange Smoothie

Prep Time: 5 minutes.

Cook Time: 0 minutes.

Serves: 2

Ingredients:

- ½ cup orange juice
- ½ cup almond milk
- ½ teaspoon vanilla extract
- ½ tablespoon honey
- 1 cup Greek yogurt
- ½ cup cauliflower, riced
- ½ navel orange, peeled and chopped
- ½ banana, peeled and chopped

Preparation:

1. Blend orange juice, almond milk and the rest of the ingredients in a blender.

2. Serve.

Serving Suggestion: Serve the smoothie with shredded chocolate on top.

Variation Tip: Add coconut cream to the smoothie.

Nutritional Information Per Serving:

Calories 178 | Fat 3.8g |Sodium 620mg | Carbs 13.3g | Fiber 2.4g | Sugar 1.2g | Protein 5.4g

Berry Smoothie

Prep Time: 5 minutes.

Cook Time: 0 minutes.

Serves: 1

Ingredi1nts:

- 1 cup frozen mixed berries
- ¼ cup sliced frozen banana
- ½ cup coconut milk
- ½ scoop vanilla whey protein

Preparation:

1. Blend berries with banana and the rest of the ingredients in a blender until smooth.
2. Serve.

Serving Suggestion: Serve the smoothie with shredded chocolate on top.

Variation Tip: Add coconut cream to the smoothie.

Nutritional Information Per Serving:

Calories 104 | Fat 31g |Sodium 834mg | Carbs 11.4g | Fiber 0.2g | Sugar 0.3g | Protein 4.6g

Pumpkin Spice Smoothie

Prep Time: 5 minutes.

Cook Time: 0 minutes.

Serves: 2

Ingredients:

Vinaigrette

- ½ cup vanilla almond milk
- ½ banana
- 2 tablespoons fat Greek yogurt
- ½ cup pumpkin puree
- 2 tablespoons calorie free pancake syrup
- 1 scoop vanilla whey protein
- ¼ teaspoons cinnamon
- ⅛ teaspoons nutmeg
- 1 pinch of cloves powder
- 1 pinch of ginger powder
- 1 cup of ice

Preparation:

1. Blend pumpkin puree, milk and the rest of the ingredients in a blender until smooth.
2. Serve.

Serving Suggestion: Serve the smoothie with shredded chocolate on top.

Variation Tip: Add coconut yogurt to the smoothie.

Nutritional Information Per Serving:

Calories 141 | Fat 24g |Sodium 547mg | Carbs 6.4g | Fiber 1.2g | Sugar 1g | Protein 10.3g

Strawberry Banana Smoothie

Prep Time: 5 minutes.

Cook Time: 0 minutes.

Serves: 2

Ingredients:

- 1 cup cashew milk
- 1 scoop vanilla whey protein powder
- 1 ripe banana, frozen
- ½ cup frozen strawberries
- ½ tablespoon chia seeds
- 1 tablespoon Nut butter

Preparation:

1. Blend strawberries, cashew milk and the rest of the ingredients in a blender until smooth.
2. Serve.

Serving Suggestion: Serve the smoothie with shredded coconut on top.

Variation Tip: Add coconut cream to the smoothie.

Nutritional Information Per Serving:

Calories 118 | Fat 5.7g |Sodium 124mg | Carbs 7g | Fiber 0.1g | Sugar 0.3g | Protein 9g

Blueberry Banana Smoothie

Prep Time: 5 minutes.

Cook Time: 0 minutes.

Serves: 2

Ingredients:

- ½ cup frozen unsweetened blueberries
- ½ medium banana, sliced and frozen
- ¾ cup plain nonfat Greek yogurt
- ¾ cup vanilla almond milk
- 2 cups ice cubes

Preparation:

1. Blend berries, yogurt and the rest of the ingredients in a blender until smooth.
2. Serve.

Serving Suggestion: Serve the smoothie with shredded chocolate on top.

Variation Tip: Add cream to the smoothie.

Nutritional Information Per Serving:

Calories 191 | Fat 2.2g |Sodium 276mg | Carbs 7.7g | Fiber 0.9g | Sugar 1.4g | Protein 8.8g

Hot Chocolate

Prep Time: 5 minutes.

Cook Time: 0 minutes.

Serves: 2

Ingredients:

- 2 cups cashew milk
- 2 tablespoons cocoa powder
- 12 drops vanilla crème stevia
- 3 drops peppermint extract

Preparation:

1. Blend cocoa powder, cashew milk and the rest of the ingredients in a blender until smooth.
2. Serve.

Serving Suggestion: Serve the hot chocolate with shredded chocolate on top.

Variation Tip: Add mini marshmallows to the drink.

Nutritional Information Per Serving:

Calories 124 | Fat 5g |Sodium 432mg | Carbs 13.1g | Fiber 0.3g | Sugar 1g | Protein 5.7g

Cucumber Gin Cocktail

. Prep Time: 5 minutes.

Cook Time: 5 minutes.

Serves: 1

Ingredients:

- 1 ounce fresh squeezed lemon juice
- 2 ounces rosemary infused stevia
- 1 ½ ounces gin
- 2 slices cucumber

Rosemary infused stevia

- 1/4 cup stevia
- 2 cups water
- 1 teaspoon rosemary

Preparation:

1. Boil 2 cups water with stevia in a pan and add rosemary.
2. Remove this mixture and leave the rosemary too steep for 2 hours.
3. Strain and mix 2 ounces of this stevia mixture with gin and lemon juice.
4. Serve with cucumber slices in the glass.

Serving Suggestion: Serve the cocktail with fresh rosemary sprig on top.

Variation Tip: Add honey to sweeten to the drink.

Nutritional Information Per Serving:

Calories 136 | Fat 10g |Sodium 249mg | Carbs 8g | Fiber 2g | Sugar 3g | Protein 4g

Lemon Drop Martini

Prep Time: 5 minutes.

Cook Time: 0 minutes.

Serves: 1

Ingredients:

- 3 tablespoons lemon juice
- 2 ½ ounces vodka
- 1 tablespoon Monk Fruit sweetener
- Lemon flavored sparkling water
- Sliced lemon peel for garnish

Preparation:

1. Mix lemon juice with vodka with sweetener, and sparkling water in a jug.
2. Serve in a glass with lemon peel on top.
3. Enjoy.

Serving Suggestion: Serve the drink with an olive skewer.

Variation Tip: Add maple syrup or honey to the drink.

Nutritional Information Per Serving:

Calories 51 | Fat 19g |Sodium 412mg | Carbs 4g | Fiber 0.3g | Sugar 1g | Protein 3g

Dessert

Chocolate Pudding Cake

Prep Time: 15 minutes.

Cook Time: 38 minutes.

Serves: 6

Ingredients:

- 3/4 cup all-purpose flour
- 3/4 cup granulated sugar
- 1 ½ teaspoon baking powder
- ½ teaspoon baking soda
- 1/4 teaspoon salt
- 1/3 cup 1/4 cup cocoa powder
- ½ cup milk
- 3 Tablespoons unsalted butter, melted
- 1 ½ teaspoon vanilla extract
- ½ cup brown sugar
- 1 3/4 cups boiling water

Preparation:

1. At 350 degrees F, preheat your oven.
2. Grease a 9-inch baking dish with cooking spray.
3. Mix 1/3 cup cocoa powder, salt, baking soda, baking powder, sugar, and flour in a bowl.
4. Stir in milk, vanilla and butter then mix well until smooth.
5. Spread this batter in the prepared baking dish.
6. Mix brown sugar with remaining ¼ cup cocoa in a small bowl.
7. Add this mixture over the batter and pour boiling water on top.
8. Bake the pudding cake for 38 minutes in the oven.
9. Allow the cake to cool and serve.

Serving Suggestion: Serve the cake with chocolate frosting on top.

Variation Tip: Add chopped berries to the cake.

Nutritional Information Per Serving:

Calories 211 | Fat 6g |Sodium 218mg | Carbs 41g | Fiber 10g | Sugar 30g | Protein 3g

Strawberry Shortcake Oatmeal

Prep Time: 15 minutes.

Cook Time: 0 minutes.

Serves: 2

Ingredients:

- 3/4 cup almond milk
- ½ cup Greek yogurt
- 1 ½ cup strawberries
- 1 cup old fashioned oats
- 1/4 cup protein powder
- 2 tablespoons sweetener
- 1/4 teaspoon salt

Preparation:

1. Smash strawberries in a bowl and stir in rest of the ingredients.
2. Add this oatmeal mixture to a mason jar and cover to seal.
3. Refrigerate this oatmeal overnight.
4. Serve.

Serving Suggestion: Serve the oatmeal with fresh berries on top.

Variation Tip: Add crushed nuts to oatmeal.

Nutritional Information Per Serving:

Calories 118 | Fat 20g |Sodium 192mg | Carbs 23.7g | Fiber 0.9g | Sugar 19g | Protein 5.2g

-

Crustless Raspberry Cheesecake

Prep Time: 15 minutes.

Cook Time: 50 minutes.

Serves: 4

Ingredients:

- 18 ounces cream cheese
- 2/3 cup Greek yogurt
- ½ cup granulated sweetener
- 1/4 cup cocoa powder
- 2 large eggs
- 1 cup raspberries
- 1/3 cup mini chocolate chips
- ¼ cup melted chocolate

Preparation:

1. At 280 degrees F, preheat your oven.
2. Add boiling water to a large baking dish to fill its bottom.
3. Place this dish in the preheated oven.
4. Grease an 8-inch cake pan with oil.
5. Beat cream cheese with sweetener and yogurt in a mixer until smooth.
6. Stir in cocoa powder and eggs then mix for 1 minute.
7. Fold in 1/3 chocolate chips and ¾ raspberries.
8. Spread this batter in the prepared cake pan and drizzle remaining chocolate chips on top.
9. Place this pan in the preheated pan in the oven.
10. Bake this batter for 50 minutes then allow it to cool.
11. Slice and serve.

Serving Suggestion: Serve the cheesecake with a scoop of vanilla cream on top.

Variation Tip: Add chopped nuts crust to the cake.

Nutritional Information Per Serving:

Calories 89 | Fat 5.8g |Sodium 95mg | Carbs 4g | Fiber 1.3g | Sugar 2g | Protein 4.9g

Protein Fudge

Prep Time: 15 minutes.

Cook Time: 0 minutes.

Serves: 8

Ingredients:

- 1 ounce mixed nuts
- 1/4 cup soy milk
- 1 tablespoon cocoa powder
- 1/3 tablespoons honey
- 1 scoop chocolate whey protein
- 2 tablespoons peanut butter

Preparation:

1. Blend nuts with milk, cocoa powder, honey, protein and peanut butter in a blender.
2. Spread this mixture in a suitable pan, lined with parchment paper.
3. Refrigerate this mixture for 1 hour.
4. Cut into squares and serve.

Serving Suggestion: Serve the fudge with chocolate or apple sauce.

Variation Tip: Add caramel sauce to the fudge.

Nutritional Information Per Serving:

Calories 117 | Fat 12g |Sodium 79mg | Carbs 24.8g | Fiber 1.1g | Sugar 18g | Protein 5g

Vanilla Egg Custards

Prep Time: 15 minutes.

Cook Time: 30 minutes.

Serves: 4

Ingredients:

- 3 cups unsweetened almond milk
- 4 eggs
- 1 scoop vanilla protein powder
- 2 teaspoons pure vanilla extract
- 1/4 teaspoon salt
- 1 teaspoon liquid vanilla stevia
- Cinnamon, to serve

Preparation:

1. At 350 degrees F, preheat your oven.
2. Warm milk in a saucepan and remove from the heat.
3. Beat eggs with stevia, vanilla extract, protein powder and salt in a blender.
4. Slowly add the hot milk and mix well.
5. Divide this mixture in 6 ramekins and place them in a 9x13 inches baking dish.
6. Drizzle cinnamon over the ramekins and add some water to the baking dish to cover its bottom.
7. Bake the custard for 30 minutes then allow them to cool.
8. Serve.

Serving Suggestion: Serve the custard with creamy frosting on top.

Variation Tip: Add chopped pecans to the custard.

Nutritional Information Per Serving:

Calories 195 | Fat 3g |Sodium 355mg | Carbs 20g | Fiber 1g | Sugar 25g | Protein 1g

Boozy Sangria Sorbet

Prep Time: 15 minutes.

Cook Time: 10 minutes.

Serves: 4

Ingredients:

- 2 cups frozen blackberries
- 3 tablespoons fruit punch
- 1/4 cup dry red wine
- 1-½ tablespoon sugar

Preparation:

1. Mix blackberries with sugar, punch and red wine in a saucepan.
2. Reduce its heat and cook for 10 minutes with occasional stirring.
3. Allow the blackberry mixture to cool then freeze for 2 hours
4. Serve.

Serving Suggestion: Serve the sorbet with chocolate syrup on top.

Variation Tip: Add dried raisins to the sorbet.

Nutritional Information Per Serving:

Calories 203 | Fat 8.9g |Sodium 340mg | Carbs 24.7g | Fiber 1.2g | Sugar 11.3g | Protein 5.3g

Strawberry Sangria Sorbet

Prep Time: 15 minutes.

Cook Time: 10 minutes.

Serves: 4

Ingredients:

- 1-lb. strawberries, hulled
- ¾ cup sugar
- 2 cups water
- ¾ cup fruity white wine

Preparation:

1. Mix strawberries with sugar, water and white wine in a saucepan.
2. Reduce its heat and cook for 10 minutes with occasional stirring.
3. Allow the strawberry mixture to cool then freeze for 1 hour
4. Serve.

Serving Suggestion: Serve the sorbet with chocolate syrup on top.

Variation Tip: Drizzle chopped berries on top.

Nutritional Information Per Serving:

Calories 153 | Fat 1g |Sodium 8mg | Carbs 66g | Fiber 0.8g | Sugar 56g | Protein 1g

Caramel Pumpkin Flan

Prep Time: 15 minutes.

Cook Time: 1 hour 5 minutes.

Serves: 8

Ingredients:

- 8 (6-ounce) ramekins
- 1 cup caramel sauce
- 1 (12-ounce) can evaporated skimmed milk
- ½ cup skim milk
- 1/4 cup sugar
- 1 egg
- 2 egg whites
- 1 ½ cups cooked pumpkin, mashed
- 1 ¼ teaspoons pumpkin pie spice
- Whipped topping

Preparation:

1. Divide the caramel sauce in each ramekin.
2. Mix ¼ cup sugar and milk in a saucepan then cook until it bubbles.
3. Remove from the heat then beat eggs with ¼ hot milk mixture in a bowl.
4. Return it to the remaining milk and add spices and pumpkin then mix well.
5. Divide this mixture in the ramekins and place the ramekins in a baking pan.
6. Pour some water to cover the bottom of the pan.
7. Cover the ramekins and bake for 1 hour at 325 degrees F.
8. Allow the ramekins to cool and cover to refrigerate for 4 hours.
9. Invert each ramekin onto a serving plate.
10. Garnish with whipped topping and cinnamon.
11. Serve.

Serving Suggestion: Serve the flan with maple syrup on top.

Variation Tip: Add crushed walnuts or pecans to the flan.

Nutritional Information Per Serving:

Calories 198 | Fat 14g |Sodium 272mg | Carbs 34g | Fiber 1g | Sugar 9.3g | Protein 1.3g

Lemon-Yogurt Mousse

Prep Time: 15 minutes.

Cook Time: 1 minute.

Serves: 2

Ingredients:

- 1 tablespoon butter
- ½ cup apricot preserves
- 1 tablespoon water
- 1/8 teaspoon ground cinnamon
- 1/8 teaspoon ground nutmeg
- 3 nectarines, quartered
- 3 peaches, quartered
- 3 plums, quartered
- 1 loaf (10-3/4 ounces) lb. cake, cubed

Preparation:

1. Beat 2 egg whites with salt, and ¼ cup sugar in a bowl and place it in a pan filled with boiling water.
2. Mix until the sugar is dissolved then remove this bowl from the heat.
3. Beat until the mixture forms peaks.
4. Add yogurt and the rest of the ingredients to a bowl and mix well.
5. Fold in egg white's mixture and mix evenly.
6. Refrigerate for 2 hours then garnish with cookies.
7. Serve.

Serving Suggestion: Serve the mousse with blackberries on top.

Variation Tip: Add berries to the mousse.

Nutritional Information Per Serving:

Calories 159 | Fat 3g |Sodium 277mg | Carbs 21g | Fiber 1g | Sugar 9g | Protein 2g

Protein Ice Cream

Prep Time: 15 minutes.

Cook Time: 0 minutes.

Serves: 1

Ingredients:

- 1 cup almond milk
- 1 scoop Sun warrior protein powder
- 1 tablespoon unsweetened cocoa powder
- 1 packet stevia
- ¼ teaspoon vanilla extract

Preparation:

1. Blend almond milk with protein powder, cocoa powder, stevia and vanilla extract in a blender.
2. Add this mixture to an ice cream maker and churn as per the machine's instructions.
3. Freeze the churned ice cream in a suitable container for 1 hour.
4. Serve.

Serving Suggestion: Serve the ice cream with chopped peanuts on top.

Variation Tip: Add crushed chocolate to the ice cream.

Nutritional Information Per Serving:

Calories 120 | Fat 3g |Sodium 122mg | Carbs 3g | Fiber 1.2g | Sugar 12g | Protein 7g

30-Days Meal Plan

Week 1

Day 1:

Breakfast: Breakfast Caprese With Eggs

Lunch: Red Lentil Dahl

Snack: Strawberry Protein Balls

Dinner: Chicken Tagine with Olives

Dessert: Chocolate Pudding Cake

Day 2:

Breakfast: Blueberry Breakfast Cake

Lunch: Baked Curried Tofu

Snack: Graham Cracker Snack

Dinner: Chicken Meatballs with Peanut Sauce

Dessert: Protein Ice Cream

Day 3:

Breakfast: Oatmeal with Crispy Bacon

Lunch: Red Cauliflower Rice

Snack: Chocolate Protein Balls

Dinner: Zucchini Noodles and Lemon Shrimp

Dessert: Lemon-Yogurt Mousse

Day 4:

Breakfast: Skillet Eggs and Chorizo

Lunch: Cauliflower Fried Rice

Snack: Ritz Cracker Snack

Dinner: BBQ Baked Pork Chops

Dessert: Caramel Pumpkin Flan

Day 5:

Breakfast: Baked Eggs and Zoodles with Avocado

Lunch: Butter Beans and Olives

Snack: Cinnamon Protein Balls

Dinner: Pork Chops & Broccoli

Dessert: Strawberry Sangria Sorbet

Day 6:

Breakfast: Spanish Tortilla with Zucchini

Lunch: Sesame Baked Tofu

Snack: Buffalo Chicken Dip

Dinner: Pistachio Pork Tenderloin with Escarole Salad

Dessert: Boozy Sangria Sorbet

Day 7:

Breakfast: Lemon Poppyseed Muffins with Blueberry Glaze

Lunch: Veggie Burgers

Snack: Baked Chicken Wings

Dinner: Skillet Pepper Steak

Dessert: Vanilla Egg Custards

Week 2

Day 1:

Breakfast: Egg Avocado Bowl

Lunch: Spaghetti & Meatballs

Snack: Avocado Toast

Dinner: Baked Sesame-Ginger Salmon

Dessert: Protein Fudge

Day 2:

Breakfast: Scrambled Tofu Burrito

Lunch: Beef Stew

Snack: Peanut Butter Protein Balls

Dinner: Pesto Shrimp with Snow Peas

Dessert: Strawberry Shortcake Oatmeal

Day 3:

Breakfast: Vegetable Frittatas

Lunch: Chipotle Baked Pork Chops

Snack: Edamame Dip

Dinner: Lemon Risotto and Shrimp

Dessert: Crustless Raspberry Cheesecake

Day 4:

Breakfast: Skillet Eggs and Chorizo

Lunch: Cauliflower Fried Rice

Snack: Ritz Cracker Snack

Dinner: BBQ Baked Pork Chops

Dessert: Caramel Pumpkin Flan

Day 5:

Breakfast: Baked Eggs and Zoodles with Avocado

Lunch: Butter Beans and Olives

Snack: Cinnamon Protein Balls

Dinner: Pork Chops & Broccoli

Dessert: Strawberry Sangria Sorbet

Day 6:

Breakfast: Spanish Tortilla with Zucchini

Lunch: Sesame Baked Tofu

Snack: Buffalo Chicken Dip

Dinner: Pistachio Pork Tenderloin with Escarole Salad

Dessert: Boozy Sangria Sorbet

Day 7:

Breakfast: Lemon Poppyseed Muffins with Blueberry Glaze

Lunch: Veggie Burgers

Snack: Baked Chicken Wings

Dinner: Skillet Pepper Steak

Dessert: Chocolate Pudding Cake

Week 3

Day 1:

Breakfast: Skillet Eggs and Chorizo

Lunch: Persian Spiced Roasted Chicken

Snack: Strawberry Protein Balls

Dinner: Chicken Tagine with Olives

Dessert: Vanilla Egg Custards

Day 2:

Breakfast: Egg Avocado Bowl

Lunch: Chicken Tagine With Olives

Snack: Graham Cracker Snack

Dinner: Chicken Meatballs with Peanut Sauce

Dessert: Boozy Sangria Sorbet

Day 3:

Breakfast: Baked Eggs and Zoodles with Avocado

Lunch: Chicken Tortilla Soup

Snack: Chocolate Protein Balls

Dinner: Zucchini Noodles and Lemon Shrimp

Dessert: Lemon-Yogurt Mousse

Day 4:

Breakfast: Breakfast Caprese With Eggs

Lunch: Harissa Chicken With Chickpeas

Snack: Ritz Cracker Snack

Dinner: BBQ Baked Pork Chops

Dessert: Protein Ice Cream

Day 5:

Breakfast: Oatmeal with Crispy Bacon

Lunch: Thai Peanut Chicken With Coconut Purple Rice

Snack: Cinnamon Protein Balls

Dinner: Pork Chops & Broccoli

Dessert: Strawberry Sangria Sorbet

Day 6:

Breakfast: Vegetable Frittatas

Lunch: Chicken Meatballs With Peanut Sauce

Snack: Buffalo Chicken Dip

Dinner: Pistachio Pork Tenderloin with Escarole Salad

Dessert: Caramel Pumpkin Flan

Day 7:

Breakfast: Scrambled Tofu Burrito

Lunch: Chicken Salad Stuffed Peppers

Snack: Baked Chicken Wings

Dinner: Skillet Pepper Steak

Dessert: Protein Fudge

Week 4

Day 1:

Breakfast: Blueberry Breakfast Cake

Lunch: Lemon-Herb Chicken And Avocado Salad

Snack: Avocado Toast

Dinner: Baked Sesame-Ginger Salmon

Dessert: Vanilla Egg Custards

Day 2:

Breakfast: Lemon Poppyseed Muffins with Blueberry Glaze

Lunch: Green Bowl With Chicken

Snack: Peanut Butter Protein Balls

Dinner: Pesto Shrimp with Snow Peas

Dessert: Strawberry Shortcake Oatmeal

Day 3:

Breakfast: Spanish Tortilla with Zucchini

Lunch: Chipotle Baked Pork Chops

Snack: Edamame Dip

Dinner: Lemon Risotto and Shrimp

Dessert: Crustless Raspberry Cheesecake

Day 4:

Breakfast: Skillet Eggs and Chorizo

Lunch: Turkey And White Bean Chili

Snack: Ritz Cracker Snack

Dinner: BBQ Baked Pork Chops

Dessert: Caramel Pumpkin Flan

Day 5:

Breakfast: Lemon Poppyseed Muffins with Blueberry Glaze

Lunch: Butter Beans and Olives

Snack: Cinnamon Protein Balls

Dinner: Pork Chops & Broccoli

Dessert: Strawberry Sangria Sorbet

Day 6:

Breakfast: Spanish Tortilla with Zucchini

Lunch: Pistachio Pork Tenderloin with Escarole Salad

Snack: Buffalo Chicken Dip

Dinner: Sesame Baked Tofu

Dessert: Boozy Sangria Sorbet

Day 7:

Breakfast: Baked Eggs and Zoodles with Avocado

Lunch: Skillet Pepper Steak

Snack: Baked Chicken Wings

Dinner: Veggie Burgers

Dessert: Vanilla Egg Custards

Conclusion

Did you like all those macro diet recipes? Do you want to have a perfect blend of carbs, proteins and fats in your diet? Well, then it's about time that you follow the above given 4-week meal plan to successfully incorporate our macro diet recipes in your daily routine. It can help you optimize the intake of these macronutrients, which will help you achieve good health. In this cookbook, you will find more than seventy delicious recipes with a 4-week meal plan to easily incorporate a macro diet into your lifestyle.

The macro diet provides a simple approach to keep track of the nutrients we consume. Instead of focusing on the caloric intakes, this diet takes the number of macronutrients like carbohydrate, proteins and fats into consideration. It is these macros that play a major role in our metabolism; carbs are an instant source of energy, proteins provide amino acids for building muscles, and fats are the long-term secondary source of energy.

By optimizing the intake of these nutrients, a person can achieve good health. According to the macro diet, there has to be a balanced intake of these macronutrients. This intake must be according to the needs of the human body. According to this diet, a meal has to have 10-35 per cent proteins, 20-35 per cent fats and 45-65 per cent carbs. Macro diet is great because it does not provide one-size-fits-all formula. Rather it offers a flexible diet plan which anyone can use according to his needs. If a person is striving for weight loss, he or she can minimize the intake of fat and carbs.

Macro-nutrients are responsible for controlling all of our metabolism. The macro diet focuses on the importance of each of these nutrients and provides them in the perfect quantity, which boosts metabolism, helps rejuvenate cells and provide energy without causing weight gain.

CPSIA information can be obtained
at www.ICGtesting.com
Printed in the USA
BVHW010350280721
613016BV00005BA/814